D0597071

DEPARTMENT OF SCIENTIFIC AND INDUSTRIAL RESEARCH

MEMOIRS OF THE GEOLOGICAL SURVEY
GREAT BRITAIN

Chemical Analyses of Igneous Rocks, Metamorphic Rocks and Minerals

1931-1954

COMPILED FROM THE
RECORDS OF THE GEOLOGICAL SURVEY

by

EILEEN M. GUPPY, B.Sc., F.G.S.

With Petrographical Descriptions by

P. A. SABINE, Ph.D., A.R.C.S.

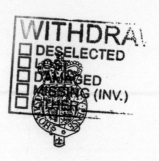
LONDON
HER MAJESTY'S STATIONERY OFFICE
1956

First published 1956
Second impression 1965
(with minor amendments)

Published by
HER MAJESTY'S STATIONERY OFFICE

To be purchased from
York House, Kingsway, London w.c.2
423 Oxford Street, London w.1
13A Castle Street, Edinburgh 2
109 St. Mary Street, Cardiff
39 King Street, Manchester 2
50 Fairfax Street, Bristol 1
35 Smallbrook, Ringway, Birmingham 5
80 Chichester Street, Belfast 1
or through any bookseller

Price 15s. 0d. net

Printed in England for Her Majesty's Stationery Office
by Lowe and Brydone (Printers) Ltd., London, N.W.10

PREFACE

SINCE the publication, in 1931, of the Geological Survey Memoir ' Chemical Analyses of Igneous Rocks, Metamorphic Rocks and Minerals ', several hundred complete and partial analyses have been made in the Chemical Laboratory of the Geological Survey. During much of this period, the conditions brought about by the second World War prevented the annual compilation of analyses in the ' Summary of Progress ' and delayed publication of memoirs, so that many of the analyses have remained unpublished. It has therefore been decided to collect together in this volume the results, published and unpublished, of analyses of igneous and metamorphic rocks and minerals carried out under the auspices of the Geological Survey. All but a few have been done in the Geological Survey Chemical Laboratory under the supervision of officers of the Government Laboratory. Mr. B. E. Dixon, who was previously in charge of the analytical work, was succeeded in 1934 by Mr. C. O. Harvey who has for varying periods had assistance from Mr. G. A. Sergeant, Mr. R. L. Hambridge, Mr. W. F. Waters, Mr. R. Sawyer, Mr. A. D. Wilson, Miss A. Shollick, Mr. K. L. H. Murray and Mr. P. Coombs. A few published analyses included in this volume have been carried out at the Chemical Research Laboratory for the Atomic Energy Division of the Geological Survey. Spectrochemical determinations have been made partly at the Government Laboratory, but during recent years a spectrographic laboratory has been established at the Geological Survey. The arrangement of analyses follows as far as possible the general style of the 1931 publication.

In the petrographical descriptions, prepared by Dr. P. A. Sabine, account has been taken of the published references and, when available, of unpublished notes by Dr. J. Phemister and Dr., now Professor, K. C. Dunham, who had charge of the Petrographical Department from 1935-1945 and 1945-1950 respectively.

W. J. PUGH

Director

Geological Survey Office
    Exhibition Road
        London, S.W.7
1st October, 1955

CONTENTS

ABBREVIATIONS

1. Abbreviations used in text

Anal.	Analyst.
M.G.S.	Memoirs of the Geological Survey. Short titles are given.
Min. Mag.	Mineralogical Magazine, London.
Min. Res.	Memoirs of the Geological Survey. Special Reports on the Mineral Resources of Great Britain.
Q.J.G.S.	Quarterly Journal of the Geological Society of London.
S.P.	Summary of Progress of the Geological Survey for the year stated, with year of publication in parentheses.
Spect. det.	Spectrochemical determination.
1-in.	The one-inch-to-one-mile map of the Geological Survey.
6-in.	Ordnance Survey map on the scale of six inches to one mile for the county named.

2. Abbreviations used in analysis tables

n.d.	Not detected.
(s)	Spectrochemical determination.
Sp. gr.	Specific gravity.

ADDITIONAL CHEMICAL DATA AND REFERENCES

SINCE this Memoir was published in 1956 a number of additional chemical or spectrographical determinations have been made. This information, together with some new references, is set out below. The bold face numbers (e.g. **620**) correspond to the numbers by which the analyses are designated in the text.

620. B:<0.002% (s). *S.P.* 1958 (1959), p. 53. **624.** *Bull. Geol. Surv. Gt. Brit.*, No. 20, 1963, p. 18. **639.** op. cit., p. 22. **642.** op. cit., p. 12. **643.** op. cit., p. 12. **647.** op. cit., p. 18. **648.** op. cit., p. 18; pl. iv, fig. 2. **651.** B:<0.002% (s). *S.P.* 1958 (1959), p. 53. **658.** V_2O_3: 0.02%. NiO: 0.03% (s). Co: 0.004% (s). **669.** V_2O_3: 0.02%. NiO: 0.006% (s). Co: 0.004% (s). *Bull. Geol. Surv. Gt. Brit.*, No. 20, 1963, p. 18; pl. iv, fig. 6. **677.** op. cit., p. 70. **680.** op. cit., p. 70. **682.** op. cit., p. 70. **687.** *For* labradorite *read* bytownite. **751.** Yt_2O_3: about 0.001% (s). *S.P.* 1955 (1956), p. 61. B:<0.002% (s). *S.P.* 1958 (1959), p. 53. **781.** *Min. Res.*, vol. xxxvii, ' Limestones of Scotland. Chemical Analyses and Petrography,' 1956, p. 23. **782.** op. cit., p. 17. **783.** op. cit., p. 28. **825.** *For* dispersionr >v *read* dispersion r>v. **830.** BaO: 0.003% (s). La_2O_3: 0.06% (s). Nb_2O_5: 0.01% (s). SrO: 0.01% (s). Yt_2O_3: 0.04% (s). ZrO_2: 0.5% (s). (Al_2O_3 reduced from 2.7 to 2.1%). *S.P.* 1958 (1959), p. 53.

CHEMICAL ANALYSES OF IGNEOUS ROCKS, METAMORPHIC ROCKS AND MINERALS

THE rock analyses are arranged primarily according to type, and, within these types, in descending order of silica percentage for the silicate rocks and increasing carbon dioxide percentage in the case of metamorphic limestones and dolomites. Minerals and the description of their properties follow the order given in Dana's ' Textbook of Mineralogy ', 4th Edition by W. E. Ford, New York and London, 1932. This arrangement of rock and mineral analyses has led to the separation of analyses of related or composite rock masses, but their interdependence has been indicated by a system of cross reference. A few partial analyses have been included in the main tables where this has appeared preferable. To avoid confusion, the bold face numbers (**1-611**), by which the analyses were designated in the 1931 memoir of chemical analyses of igneous rocks, metamorphic rocks and minerals, have been continued in numerical sequence in the present memoir.

The name under which a rock or mineral was previously described has as far as possible been retained, but when a new name has been substituted the original appears in inverted commas. The name is followed by the geological occurrence and age, the locality of each specimen and the numbers of the appropriate one-inch-to-one-mile geological and six-inch Ordnance Survey maps. When given alone the one-inch number signifies one of the English and Welsh series; Scottish maps are followed by the abbreviation ' Scot.' and Irish maps by ' Ire.' These numbers are followed, in parentheses, by the registered number of the analysis and name of the analyst.

Numbers prefixed by E, S, NI and F refer respectively to specimens and corresponding thin sections in the English and Welsh, Scottish, Northern Irish and Foreign collections housed in the Geological Survey and Museum. Numbers preceded by MI refer to specimens in the Mineral Inventory.

Reference is made to the first publication, if any, of an analysis and its quotation in the appropriate Geological Survey Memoir. Reference has also been given to figured micro-sections.

I. ANALYSES OF IGNEOUS ROCKS

GRANITES, GRANOPHYRE, PEGMATITE

	GRANITES AND GRANOPHYRE			
	612	613	614	615
SiO_2	77·52	77·06	75·80	73·17
Al_2O_3	12·10	11·90	13·04	12·95
Fe_2O_3	0·38	0·27	0·03	1·45
FeO	0·66	1·17	1·25	2·06
MgO	0·21	0·16	0·19	0·08
CaO	0·51	0·71	0·41	1·30
Na_2O	3·36	3·44	3·20	4·37
K_2O	4·78	4·94	4·85	3·67
$H_2O > 105°C$	0·28	0·38	0·67	0·43
$H_2O < 105°C$	0·15	0·07	0·12	0·14
TiO_2	0·07	0·13	0·11	0·39
P_2O_5	0·01	0·01	0·18	0·07
MnO	0·02	0·02	0·03	0·11
CO_2	tr.	tr.	tr.	0·10
Cl	n.d.	n.d.	0·03	—
F	—	—	n.d.	—
S	0·03	0·02	tr.	—
Sulphide S	—	—	tr.	—
FeS_2	—	—	—	n.d.
Cr_2O_3	n.d. ($<0·01$)	n.d. ($<0·01$)	n.d.	—
BaO	0·02	0·03	n.d.	—
Li_2O	0·023(s)	0·014(s)	—	—
Rb_2O	0·045(s)	0·036(s)	—	—
Cs_2O	n.d. ($<0·02$;s)	n.d. ($<0·02$;s)	—	—
TOTAL	100·17	100·36	99·91	100·29
Less O for Cl, S	—	—	0·01	—
	100·17	100·36	99·90	100·29
Sp. gr.	2·63	2·63	2·63	—

612. Granite. ' Aplitic granite ' of Mourne Mountains granite mass, Tertiary. Slieve Binnian tunnel, Silent Valley entrance, Mourne Mountains, Co. Down. 1-in. 60 Ire., 6-in. 53 S.W. (1635. Anal., A. D. Wilson and P. Coombs; spect. det., C. O. Harvey and K. L. H. Murray).
N I 81. A fine-grained grey granite composed of microperthite, fresh oligoclase, quartz in allotriomorphic crystals and micrographically intergrown with ortho- clase, and greenish-brown biotite. Colourless fluorite, magnetite and zircon are accessory. The orthoclase is partly altered to a very finely disseminated dusky montmorillonoid.
S.P. 1953 (1954), p. 63. *Bull. Geol. Surv. Gt. Brit.*, No. 8, 1955, p. 19.
See also No. **613**.

613. Granite. ' Quartzose granite ' of Mourne Mountains granite mass, Tertiary. Slieve Binnian tunnel, 907 yd from Annalong end, Mourne Mountains, Co. Down. 1-in. 60 Ire., 6-in. 53 N.W. (1636. Anal., A. D. Wilson and P. Coombs; spect. det., C. O. Harvey and K. L. H. Murray).

N I 453. A grey granite composed of coarse allotriomorphic crystals of micro-perthite often a centimetre across, oligoclase and allotriomorphic quartz some-times graphically intergrown with the microperthite, and partly chloritized brown biotite. The orthoclase is clouded with minute dusky alteration products probably montmorillonoid.
S.P. 1953 (1954), p. 63. *Bull. Geol. Surv. Gt. Brit.*, No. 8, 1955, p. 19.
See also No. **612.**

614. **Granite.** Eskdale Granite, normal type; post-Borrowdale Volcanic Series (Ordovician), probably Old Red Sandstone. Quarry 620 yd due S. of Mun-caster Fell, Murthwaite Bridge, Miterdale, Cumberland. 1-in. 38, 6-in. 82 N.E. (1007. Anal., C. O. Harvey).
cf. E 16855. A fairly coarse-grained pinkish-grey granite composed of micro-perthite, enclosing and interlocked with quartz, oligoclase, muscovite, chloritized biotite and pseudomorphs in a finely divided muscovite aggregate. Purple fluorite, biotite and zircon are accessory.
S.P. 1936, Pt. I (1937), p. 86. *M.G.S.* ' Gosforth ', 1937, p. 128.
See also No. **644.**

615. **Granophyre.** Carrock Fell Complex, post-Borrowdale Volcanic Series (Ordo-vician), probably Old Red Sandstone. 600 yd E. of trigonometrical height 2174, Carrock Fell, Cumberland. 1-in. 23, 6-in. 48 S.W. (944. Anal., B. E. Dixon).
E 16184. A dark pinkish-grey granophyre composed of scattered tablets of albite-oligoclase, zoned to albite, set with sometimes rounded idiomorphic prisms of hedenbergite and small needles of hornblende in a matrix of micro-pegmatite among which oxidized ore and fibrous hornblendic and chloritic materials are distributed. Apatite is accessory.
S.P. 1933, Pt. I (1934), p. 91.
See also Nos. **629, 650, 675, 688, 706, 743-4.**

616. **Granite.** Probably Permian or late Pennsylvanian. Smith Granite Co. quarry, Westerly, Rhode Island, United States of America. (1544. Anal., W. F. Waters and P. Coombs; spect. det., C. O. Harvey).
cf. F 5814. A fine-grained grey granite composed of quartz, microcline and oligoclase, with small amounts of biotite and muscovite and accessory apatite and iron ore.
This rock was analysed as part of the investigation sponsored by various American institutions into the precision and accuracy in chemical, spectro-graphical and modal analysis of silicate rocks.
Bull. U.S. Geol. Surv., No. 980, 1951, p. 9. ' *Quantitative spectrochemical analysis of silicates* ', L. H. Ahrens, 1954, p. 23. London.

617. **Granite.** Part of injection and permeation zone, Shetland Metamorphic Series. South side of road midway between Sae Water and Loch of Voe, Voe, Delting, Shetland. 1-in. 128 Scot., 6-in. 37 N.E. (1064. Anal., C. O. Harvey; spect. det., H. K. Whalley and J. W. J. Fay).
S 33682. A grey muscovite-biotite-granite in which the dominant feldspar is microcline. There is a little orthoclase and oligoclase. Muscovite sometimes forms symplektitic intergrowths with oligoclase. Garnet and apatite are accessory.

618. **Soda-granite** (trondhjemite). Ballantrae Igneous Complex, Ordovician. Summit of Byne Hill, 2¼ miles S. of Girvan Harbour, Ayrshire. 1-in. 7 Scot., 6-in. 55 S.W. (906. Anal., B. E. Dixon).
S 27367. A grey fine-grained rock composed of idiomorphic albite prisms, granular quartz sometimes with sutured margins, orthoclase, deep-brown biotite moulded upon quartz and feldspar, and bluish-green and brown hornblende. Small quantities of opaque iron ore are present and there are occasional prisms of zircon and apatite.
S.P. 1931, Pt. I (1932), p. 79. *Geol. Mag.*, vol. lxix, 1932, p. 129.
See also Nos. **686, 696, 710, 728.**

	GRANITES				PEGMATITE
	616	617	618	619	620
SiO_2 ..	72·45	71·22	70·18	70·04	71·84
Al_2O_3 ..	14·13	14·30	14·24	10·53	17·48
Fe_2O_3 ..	0·80	0·16	0·16	3·00	0·19
FeO	0·93	2·18	4·64	4·61	0·12
MgO ..	0·38	0·79	0·71	tr.	0·13
CaO ..	1·34	1·52	1·44	0·27	1·65
Na_2O ..	3·50*	2·97	6·09	5·00	4·80
K_2O ..	5·71*	4·70	0·73	4·36	2·77
$H_2O>105°C$	0·33	0·88	0·88	0·20	0·92
$H_2O<105°C$	0·02	0·07	0·34	0·61	0·18
TiO_2 ..	0·26	0·32	0·46	0·20	0·04
P_2O_5 ..	0·12	0·30	0·23	tr.	0·02
MnO ..	0·03	0·18	—	0·09	tr.
CO_2	—	0·10	tr.	0·07	n.d.
F	—	—	—	0·41	—
S	0·02	0·01	—	tr.	0·01
FeS_2 ..	—	—	0·19	—	—
Cr_2O_3 ..	0·01	n.d.	—	—	n.d.
BaO ..	0·10	0·04	—	—	0·17
SrO	—	0·01(s)	—	—	—
Li_2O ..	—	—	tr.	tr.	—
Rb_2O ..	—	0·02(s)	—	—	—
Rarer oxides	—	—	—	—	0·07(s)§
TOTAL	100·13*†	99·77	100·29	100·22‡	100·39
Less O for S, F	0·01	—	—	0·17	—
	100·12	99·77	100·29	100·05	100·39
Sp. gr. ..	—	—	—	—	2·63

* Amended figures.
† Semi-quantitative spect. det. percentages:—Ga: 0·001. La: 0·01. Sr: 0·02. Yt: <0·002. Zr: 0·03.
‡ Including:—ZrO_2: 0·25. SnO_2: 0·10. ThO_2: 0·03. Rare earth oxides: 0·07. Ta_2O_5: 0·03. Nb_2O_5: 0·33. U_3O_8: 0·02.
§ Present in approximately the following percentages:—MnO: 0·007. ZrO_2: 0·01. SrO: 0·05. Ga_2O_3: 0·004. Yt_2O_3: <0·01.

619. Albite-riebeckite-granite. ' Younger Granite' suite of Nigeria, post-Pre-Cambrian, pre-Upper Cretaceous. Kaffo Valley, Liruei Hills, Kano Province, Nigeria. (Anal., Chemical Research Laboratory).
A pale rock composed of coarse plates of microperthite and allotriomorphic quartz enclosing, and cemented by, small tablets of albite. Riebeckite and aegirine are moulded upon the feldspar and there are minor amounts of pyrochlore, cryolite and topaz.
M.G.S. ' The Petrography of some of the Riebeckite-Granites of Nigeria ', 1952, p. 33.

620. Muscovite-oligoclase-quartz-pegmatite. ' Regional pegmatite suite'. Thick vein cutting striped, locally-injected Moine pelitic schist. 1000 yd E. 45° S. of trigonometrical height 1835 (summit) of Meall a'Bhainne, near Loch Shiel, Argyllshire. 1-in. 62 Scot., 6-in. 4 S.E. (1650. Anal., A. D. Wilson and P. Coombs; spect. det., C. O. Harvey and K. L. H. Murray).
S 40422. A cream-coloured pegmatite composed of coarse interlocking muscovite, oligoclase, orthoclase and quartz. Rare small cubes of magnetite are present.
S.P. 1954 (1955), p. 60.

PORPHYRIES

621. Trondhjemite-porphyry. Irregular intrusion cutting permeation granite-gneiss (Moine pelitic host). Allt an Fhaing, 1100 yd S. 34° W. of Callop, near Loch Shiel, Argyllshire. 1-in. 62 Scot., 6-in. 5 S.W. (1651. Anal., A. D. Wilson and P. Coombs; spect. det., C. O. Harvey and K. L. H. Murray).

S 40423. A pale-grey rock containing coarse crystals of oligoclase, sometimes rimmed by myrmekite and sometimes rich in white mica, and occasional small allotriomorphic garnets, in a base of quartz, oligoclase and orthoclase with plentiful biotite arranged in parallel orientation. The biotite mainly occurs in small tablets but sometimes forms large irregular crystals associated with iron ore and apatite. Orthite is a scarce accessory.

S.P. 1954 (1955), p. 60.

622. Trondhjemite-porphyry. Intrusion cutting Moine Schists. Road cutting 730 yd N. 10° E. of trigonometrical height 356, Tom na Dubh Ghlaic, 300 yd E. of Acharn Bridge, Argyllshire. 1-in. 52 Scot., 6-in. 55 N.W. (1043. Anal., C. O. Harvey).

S 32457. A schistose grey rock composed of phenocrysts of oligoclase, often zoned, with rare phenocrysts of orthoclase and numerous irregular elongate crystals of biotite arranged in a roughly parallel fashion in a fine-grained granular groundmass of quartz, untwinned acid plagioclase and a little ortho-clase. Apatite, muscovite, zircon, chlorite and a little hydrated iron ore are accessory.

S.P. 1938 (1940), p. 95.

	PORPHYRIES			
	621	622	623	624
SiO_2	73·76	72·13	72·10	68·83
Al_2O_3	14·79	15·26	12·04	14·29
Fe_2O_3	0·17	n.d.	4·63	0·84
FeO	0·81	1·72	0·29	1·72
MgO	0·23	0·72	0·29	1·60
CaO	1·64	2·14	1·11	2·78
Na_2O	4·98	5·23	3·20	4·35
K_2O	3·30	2·10	5·31	3·88
$H_2O > 105°C$	0·26	0·40	tr.	0·48
$H_2O < 105°C$	0·06	0·09	0·12	0·08
TiO_2	0·08	0·34	0·35	0·79
P_2O_5	0·03	0·08	0·10	0·65
MnO	0·06	0·03	0·04	0·07
CO_2	n.d.	tr.	0·34	tr.
S	0·02	tr.	—	—
FeS_2	—	—	0·07	0·09
Cr_2O_3	n.d.	n.d.	tr.	—
BaO	0·11	0·07	—	—
Rarer oxides	0·06(s)*	—	—	—
TOTAL	100·36	100·31	99·99	100·45
Sp. gr.	2·64	2·66	—	—

* Present in approximately the following percentages:—ZrO_2: 0·01. SrO: 0·05. Ga_2O_3: 0·004. Yt_2O_3: <0·01.

623. Quartz-porphyry. Intrusion or lava. South-westernmost hill, Mabeleapudi Hills (Kopjes) about 17 miles S. of Ngami, Bechuanaland Protectorate, South Africa. (972. Anal., B. E. Dixon).

F 3696. A dark-grey quartz-porphyry composed of phenocrysts of quartz, microperthite and scarce oligoclase with pseudomorphs in granular epidote, probably after pyroxene, in a fine-grained quartzo-feldspathic groundmass rich in opaque iron ore granules and displaying a well-marked fluxion structure. Feldspar and epidote phenocrysts form cumulophyric aggregates. Carbonate, muscovite and zircon are accessory.
S.P. 1934, Pt. I (1935), p. 83. *Trans. Roy. Soc. South Africa*, vol. xxiii, 1936, p. 171.

624. Granodiorite-porphyry. Dyke or sheet cutting granodiorite of Strontian Granite Complex; post-Moine, pre-Middle Old Red Sandstone. Coast, 300 yd N. of Eilean a' Mhuirich, Loch Sunart, Argyllshire. 1-in. 52 Scot., 6-in. 27 S.E. (947. Anal., B. E. Dixon).
S 28450. A grey granodiorite-porphyry with phenocrysts of oligoclase and perthitic orthoclase, up to about one centimetre long, in a groundmass of frequently tabular oligoclase and scarce orthoclase, of average size about 0·3 mm, with interstitial quartz and a little micropegmatite. Biotite and hornblende are common and there is some chlorite, probably pseudomorphous after hornblende. Sphene, zircon, orthite, ilmenite, magnetite and apatite are accessory.
S.P. 1933, Pt. I (1934), p. 91.
See also Nos. **639, 642, 648.**

RHYOLITES, FELSITES AND OBSIDIANS

625. Riebeckite-felsite. Dyke cutting granite; ? Old Red Sandstone. Beorgs of Uyea, 435 yd W. 10° S. of outflow from Mill Loch, North Roe, Shetland. 1-in. 130 Scot., 6-in. 14 N.E. (962. Anal., B. E. Dixon).
S 29707. A grey granophyric riebeckite-felsite composed of abundant prisms of riebeckite and aegirine set with a little epidote in a granophyric groundmass of quartz and alkali-feldspar.
S.P. 1933, Pt. I (1934), p. 90. *Min. Mag.*, vol. xxix, 1950, p. 366.

626. Riebeckite-felsite. Dyke cutting granite; ? Old Red Sandstone. Beorgs of Uyea, 335 yd S.W. of outflow from Mill Loch, North Roe, Shetland. 1-in. 130 Scot., 6-in. 14 N.E. (960. Anal., B. E. Dixon).
S 29704. A grey granophyric spherulitic riebeckite-felsite with numerous pink feldspar phenocrysts. The rock is composed of phenocrysts of soda-orthoclase and corroded but otherwise idiomorphic phenocrysts of quartz set in a groundmass of micropegmatite spherulites cemented by granular quartz and alkali-feldspar. Needles and robust prisms of aegirine and riebeckite are abundant.
S.P. 1933, Pt. I (1934), p. 90. *Min. Mag.*, vol. xxix, 1950, p. 366.

627. Felsite. Dyke cutting granite; ? Old Red Sandstone. Beorgs of Uyea, 350 yd W. 31° S. of outflow from Mill Loch, North Roe, Shetland. 1-in. 130 Scot., 6-in. 14 N.E. (959. Anal., B. E. Dixon).
S 29703. A brownish-green spherulitic felsite composed of abundant green needles up to 0·1 mm in length, perhaps of chloritoid, set with granular epidote and ore in a micropegmatitic to spherulitic base of quartz and alkali-feldspar.
S.P. 1933, Pt. I (1934), p. 90. *Min. Mag.*, vol. xxix, 1950, p. 366.

628. Felsite. Intrusion in Dalradian Series; ? Lower Old Red Sandstone. Quarry, 350 yd W. of Crossley, Kincardineshire. 1-in. 67 Scot., 6-in. 10 N.E. (980. Anal., C. O. Harvey).
S 30693. A pink felsite composed of an interlocking microgranitic groundmass of quartz, orthoclase and albite with grain size often about 0·07 mm, numerous flakes of muscovite and rare phenocrysts of microperthite. There are a few spherulitic intergrowths of quartz and feldspar. A little carbonate is accessory.

		FELSITES			
	625	626	627	628	629
SiO_2 ..	76·20	76·13	75·88	75·14	67·37
Al_2O_3 ..	11·03	11·21	11·19	14·13	17·94
Fe_2O_3	1·58	1·66	2·44	0·43	0·56
FeO	1·45	1·45	1·10	0·22	1·86
MgO ..	0·12	0·11	0·15	0·10	2·55
CaO ..	0·20	0·25	0·44	0·55	0·73
Na_2O ..	4·90	4·30	4·04	4·47	2·14
K_2O ..	4·39	4·39	4·39	4·27	4·39
$H_2O>105°C$	0·14	0·13	0·12	0·41	2·15
$H_2O<105°C$	0·05	0·04	0·07	0·06	0·15
TiO_2 ..	0·24	0·28	0·31	0·06	0·07
P_2O_5 ..	0·15	0·17	tr.	0·03	0·07
MnO ..	0·05	0·06	0·06	0·03	0·03
CO_2	tr.	tr.	n.d.	0·31	0·10
Cl	—	—	—	tr.	—
FeS_2 ..	—	—	—	0·06	0·08
BaO ..	—	—	—	0·01	—
TOTAL	100·50	100·18	100·19	100·28	100·19

629. Felsite. Carrock Fell Complex, post-Borrowdale Volcanic Series (Ordovician), probably Old Red Sandstone. Dump from old level at head of Long Grain, 550 yd W. 34° S. of trigonometrical height 2157 at summit of High Pike, Cumberland. 1-in. 23, 6-in. 47 S.E. (945. Anal., B. E. Dixon).
E 16185. A pale-grey felsite or quartz-feldspar-porphyry with numerous corroded phenocrysts of quartz showing remains of idiomorphic form, hypidiomorphic phenocrysts of perthitic orthoclase and anorthoclase in a sericitized felsitic groundmass. Veinlets traversing the rock contain pyrite, chlorite, carbonate, quartz and kaolinite.
S.P. 1933, Pt. I (1934), p. 91.
See also Nos. **615, 650, 675, 688, 706, 743-4.**

630. Porphyritic obsidian. Tertiary. 63 ft deep, Sandy Braes No. 4 Borehole, Tardree Mountain, Co. Antrim. 1-in. 28 Ire., 6-in. 44 N.E. (1611. Anal., R. Sawyer, K. L. H. Murray and P. Coombs; spect. det., C. O. Harvey and K. L. H. Murray).
N I 370. A fresh black perlitic obsidian composed of rounded phenocrysts of quartz and subangular phenocrysts of sanidine and albite set in a brown glassy base having a marked perlitic structure. There are occasional phenocrysts of pleochroic orthite and a little accessory opaque iron ore.
S.P. 1952 (1953), p. 49.

631. Rhyolite. Tertiary lava. 70 ft 6 in.–73 ft deep, Upton Park No. 1 Borehole, 440 yd W.N.W. of Templepatrick Railway Station, Co. Antrim. 1-in. 28 Ire., 6-in. 51 S.W. (1609. Anal., A. D. Wilson, K. L. H. Murray and P. Coombs; spect. det., C. O. Harvey and K. L. H. Murray).
N I 361. White rhyolite containing rounded phenocrysts of quartz and angular phenocrysts of albite and sanidine set in a microcrystalline quartzo-feldspathic groundmass containing a little chlorite and dark-green biotite. There are a few very narrow veinlets of stilbite. There are numerous clusters of minute granules, perhaps ore.
S.P. 1952 (1953), p. 48.

632. Rhyolite. Tertiary lava. 193 ft 3 in.–196 ft 5 in. deep, Upton Park No. 3 Borehole, 950 yd W.N.W. of Templepatrick Railway Station, Co. Antrim. 1-in. 28 Ire.,

6-in. 50 S.E. (1613. Anal., A. D. Wilson, K. L. H. Murray and P. Coombs; spect. det., C. O. Harvey and K. L. H. Murray).
N I 372. A pale-mauve rhyolite composed of idiomorphic phenocrysts of sanidine and oligoclase, scarce rounded phenocrysts of quartz and rare limonitized ferromagnesian phenocrysts set in a fine-grained quartzo-feldspathic groundmass in which there are scattered flakes of biotite and plentiful clusters of minute granules, perhaps ore.
S.P. 1952 (1953), p. 49.

	OBSIDIANS AND RHYOLITES				
	630	631	632	633	634
SiO_2	74·95	73·18	72·43	71·96	66·10
Al_2O_3	11·77	13·68	13·56	13·77	12·99
Fe_2O_3	1·03	0·41	0·53	2·03	1·74
FeO	0·72	0·50	0·26	0·20	n.d.
MgO	0·01	0·21	0·90	0·12	1·68
CaO	1·02	1·12	0·67	0·91	2·55
Na_2O	2·82	3·67	3·48	2·65	0·95
K_2O	4·70	4·33	3·89	6·79	1·25
$H_2O > 105°C$	2·76	2·10	1·61	0·75	6·25
$H_2O < 105°C$	0·44	0·75	2·49	0·52	6·57
TiO_2	0·12	tr.	tr.	0·14	0·14
P_2O_5	0·06	0·05	0·05	0·05	0·03
MnO	0·04	0·06	0·06	0·03	0·06
CO_2	n.d.	n.d.	n.d.	n.d.	tr.
S	0·01	0·02	0·01	0·03	0·01
Cr_2O_3	tr.	n.d.	n.d.	tr.	tr.
BaO	0·02	0·01	0·01	0·03	0·01
Li_2O	0·002(s)	0·05(s)	0·05(s)	0·003(s)	0·007(s)
Rb_2O	0·01(s)	0·05(s)	0·05(s)	0·02(s)	0·003(s)
Cs_2O	n.d. ($<0·01$; s)	n.d. ($<0·01$; s)	n.d. ($<0·01$; s)	n.d. ($<0·02$; s)	n.d. ($<0·01$; s)
TOTAL	100·48	100·19	100·05	100·00	100·34
Sp. gr.	2·42	2·52	2·52	2·59	2·29

633. Porphyritic obsidian, devitrified. Tertiary. 99 ft deep, Sandy Braes No. 2 Borehole, Tardree Mountain, Co. Antrim. 1-in. 28 Ire., 6-in. 44 N.E. (1610. Anal., R. Sawyer, K. L. H. Murray and P. Coombs; spect. det., C. O. Harvey and K. L. H. Murray).
N I 369. A mottled pink devitrified porphyritic obsidian composed of numerous mainly rounded quartz phenocrysts and scarce rounded phenocrysts of albite and sanidine set in a microcrystalline felsitic groundmass of devitrified glass showing fluxion structure and enclosing abundant minute ore granules. There are numerous small veinlets and patches of stilbite.
S.P. 1952 (1953), p. 48.

634. Porphyritic obsidian, devitrified. Tertiary. 100 ft deep, Sandy Braes No. 5 Borehole, Tardree Mountain, Co. Antrim. 1-in. 28 Ire., 6-in. 44 N.E. (1612. Anal., R. Sawyer, K. L. H. Murray and P. Coombs; spect. det., C. O. Harvey and K. L. H. Murray).
N I 371. A powdery buff-coloured partly devitrified porphyritic obsidian composed of corroded phenocrysts of quartz and hypidiomorphic phenocrysts of oligoclase and sanidine in a groundmass of glass mainly altered to rounded and irregular patches of a microcrystalline montmorillonoid and showing a fluxion structure.
S.P. 1952 (1953), p. 49.

BOSTONITE, TRACHYTE, MONZONITE AND ALKALI-SYENITE

635. Bostonite. Dyke cutting Old Red Sandstone. Scorra Dale, Orphir, Orkney. 1-in. 119 Scot., 6-in. 107 S.W. (910. Anal., B. E. Dixon).
S 27536. A medium-grey rock, related to the camptonites, containing abundant laths of feldspar, mainly acid plagioclase, set in a fine-grained groundmass of alkali-feldspar, chlorite, granular iron ore and carbonate. Ferromagnesian phenocrysts, including hornblende, have been entirely replaced by calcite, and there are a few amygdales also containing this mineral.
S.P. 1931, Pt. I (1932), p. 79. *M.G.S.* ' Orkneys ', 1935, p. 178.

636. Trachyte. Elongate mass intrusive in Tertiary plateau basalt lavas; Tertiary. Crag on S. side of Lochan a' Bhuinn-a'-Sè, N. end of Cnoc Carach, 2¼ miles W. of Kinlochaline, Morvern, Argyllshire. 1-in. 52 Scot., 6-in. 54 S.E. (927. Anal., B. E. Dixon).
S 28389. A grey rock composed of scarce tabular phenocrysts of perthitic feldspar showing complicated twinning, abundant smaller zoned acid plagioclase laths and irregular biotite crystals, crowded with granular iron ore, in a trachytic groundmass of orthoclase, acid plagioclase, elongate sodic pyroxene prisms and abundant small ore granules. Rather turbid apatite needles are common.
S.P. 1932, Pt. I (1933), p. 95.

	BOSTONITE	TRACHYTE	MONZONITE	ALKALI-SYENITE
	635	636	637	638
SiO_2	49·25	60·45	54·05	52·33
Al_2O_3	18·45	17·35	15·13	17·86
Fe_2O_3	0·63	2·52	4·28	3·12
FeO	4·09	1·96	4·42	3·89
MgO	3·88	1·30	3·69	3·61
CaO	6·43	2·04	7·03	1·88
Na_2O	3·31	6·84	4·13	3·04
K_2O	3·83	5·51	4·46	7·79
$H_2O > 105°C$	3·25	0·58	0·52	3·05
$H_2O < 105°C$	0·75	0·13	0·06	1·02
TiO_2	0·87	0·95	1·31	1·17
P_2O_5	0·80	0·48	0·78	0·46
MnO	—	0·20	0·18	0·08
CO_2	3·86	tr.	tr.	0·26
Cl	—	—	—	tr.
S	—	—	—	0·02
FeS_2	0·40	0·07	0·04	—
Cr_2O_3	—	—	—	n.d.
BaO	—	—	—	0·19
Li_2O	—	—	—	tr.
Rare earths	—	—	tr.	—
TOTAL	99·80	100·38	100·08	99·77
Sp. gr.	—	—	—	2·62

637. Monzonite, possibly a hybrid rock. Foliated hornblendic edge of the Hildasay granitic syenitic mass, ? pre-Old Red Sandstone. ' Later Granite '. Shore 300 yd S. 35° W. of pier, Hamnavoe, West Burra, Shetland. 1-in. 126 Scot., 6-in. 56 S.W. (929. Anal., B. E. Dixon).
S 28391. A mottled pink and green rock composed of irregular hornblende prisms and pyroxene prisms enclosing hornblende, with occasional coarse-grained microcline-microperthite in a groundmass of interlocking microcline,

oligoclase and microcline-microperthite grains. Iron ore is often in aggregates with hornblende; idiomorphic crystals of sphene, irregular coarse-grained epidote, prisms of apatite and flakes of muscovite and biotite are common accessories.
S.P. 1932, Pt. I (1933), p. 96.
See also Nos. **645, 649.**

638. Nepheline-syenite, ' potash alkali-syenite '. Syenitic segregation in the Lugar Sill, Carboniferous or Permian. 554 ft 6 in. deep, No. 16 Borehole, Lands of Mortonmuir, 1 mile 725 yd E. 12° S. of Darnconner Church and 750 yd W. 18° N. of Mortonmuir Farm, Cronberry, Lugar, Ayrshire. 1-in. 14 Scot., 6-in. 30 S.W. (1447. Anal., G. A. Sergeant).
S 36045. A mottled pink and grey nepheline-syenite composed of turbid idiomorphic nepheline, interlocking plates of microperthite, clear andesine and interstitial analcite, carbonate and bowlingite. There are many small tablets of biotite, crystals of iron ore, barkevikite prisms and accessory apatite.
Trans. Geol. Soc. Glasgow, vol. xxi, 1948, p. 165.
See also Nos. **718-9.**

GRANODIORITES AND DIORITES

639. Adamellite. Steeply inclined sheet, Strontian Granite Complex, post-Moine, pre-Middle Old Red Sandstone. Quarry at Kingairloch Pier, 1670 yd S. 7° W. of trigonometrical height 2136, Beinn na Cille, Loch a' Choire, Morvern, Argyllshire. 1-in. 52 Scot., 6-in. 42 S.E. (976. Anal., B. E. Dixon).
S 30277. A pinkish-grey rock consisting of large plates of microperthite which enclose and interlock with prisms of oligoclase and orthoclase, together with allotriomorphic granular quartz and clots of chloritized biotite. Sphene, apatite, ilmenite, magnetite and pyrite are accessory.
Trans. Roy. Soc. Edin., vol. lxi, 1948, p. 543. *Q.J.G.S.,* vol. cvi for 1950, 1951, p. 328.
See also Nos. **624, 642, 648.**

640. Granodiorite. Caledonian sill in Moine Schists, acid member of appinite suite. East side of Beinn Gàire, 1000 yd N. 6° W. of N. end of Lochan Dubh, Moidart, Inverness-shire. 1-in. 52 Scot., 6-in. 149 N.E. (1019. Anal., C. O. Harvey).
S 31739. A fine-grained grey granodiorite composed of interlocking granular crystals of quartz, orthoclase and oligoclase with numerous biotite crystals of similar size moulded upon them. The feldspar tends to form microphenocrysts. A little muscovite, chlorite, zircon and apatite are accessory.
S.P. 1937 (1938), p. 96.

641. Adamellite. Intrusion in Dalradian Series; ' Older Granite '. Badentoy Old Quarry, 100 yd W.N.W. of Redmire, Mary Culter, Kincardineshire. 1-in. 67 Scot., 6-in. 7 S.W. (981. Anal., C. O. Harvey).
S 30694. A pale medium-grained muscovite-biotite-adamellite containing oligoclase-andesine, orthoclase and plentiful microcline. Quartz forms a mosaic of irregular interlocking crystals. Biotite is partly altered to chlorite. Apatite, zircon and magnetite are accessory.

642. Tonalite, ' tonalitic granodiorite '. Outer member of Strontian Granite Complex, post-Moine, pre-Middle Old Red Sandstone. In burn 900 yd W. 30° S. of Bellsgrove Lodge, Sunart, Argyllshire. 1-in. 52 Scot., 6-in. 28 N.W. (946. Anal., B. E. Dixon).
S 28448. A coarse grey tonalite composed of allotriomorphic crystals of andesine zoned to oligoclase, quartz and orthoclase, with deep-brown biotite and hornblende as the main ferromagnesian minerals. Interstitial myrmekitic intergrowths of quartz and andesine are plentiful. Sphene, apatite, zircon and a little carbonate are accessory.
S.P. 1933, Pt. I (1934), p. 91.
See also Nos. **624, 639, 648.**

ADAMELLITES, TONALITES AND GRANODIORITE

	639	640	641	642	643	644
SiO_2	71·25	71·01	69·63	66·58	66·53	65·09
Al_2O_3	14·33	15·84	15·27	14·84	15·58	16·84
Fe_2O_3	0·19	0·27	0·39	0·15	1·01	0·29
FeO	1·45	1·28	2·64	2·94	1·97	3·64
MgO	1·18	0·44	0·87	2·22	1·93	0·94
CaO	2·12	2·31	2·18	3·58	2·99˙	3·33
Na_2O	3·92	3·97	3·60	4·48	4·79	3·32
K_2O	4·10	4·09	3·71	2·87	2·56	4·17
$H_2O > 105°C$	0·47	0·50	0·62	0·68	1·01	1·32
$H_2O < 105°C$	0·05	0·11	0·10	0·14	0·69	0·13
TiO_2	0·34	0·23	0·62	1·04	0·60	0·49
P_2O_5	0·58	0·05	0·22	0·49	0·28	0·23
MnO	0·03	0·05	0·04	0·05	0·04	0·13
CO_2	tr.	tr.	0·14	tr.	0·03	tr.
ZrO_2	—	—	tr.	—	—	—
Cl	tr.	—	—	—	—	0·07
F	—	—	—	—	—	n.d.
S	—	tr.	—	—	0·01	0·01
Sulphide S	—	—	—	—	—	tr.
FeS_2	0·03	—	0·04	0·18	—	—
Cr_2O_3	—	—	—	—	n.d.	n.d.
BaO	—	0·10	0·07	—	0·07	0·05
Li_2O	tr.	—	—	—	—	—
TOTAL	100·04	100·25	100·14	100·24	100·09	100·05
Less O for Cl	—	—	—	—	—	0·02
	100·04	100·25	100·14	100·24	100·09	100·03
Sp. gr.	—	2·64	—	—	2·64	2·72

643. Tonalite. Contact-altered tonalite, margin of quartz-dolerite boss (probably Permo-Carboniferous) in outer member of Strontian Granite Complex (post-Moine, pre-Middle Old Red Sandstone). 1300 yd·N. 20° W. of Longrigg, near Strontian, Argyllshire. 1-in. 52 Scot., 6-in. 27 N.E. (1042. Anal., C. O. Harvey). S 30208. A dark-grey tonalite composed of coarse allotriomorphic crystals of andesine, quartz and orthoclase with abundant fine-grained micrographic intergrowths of quartz and alkali-feldspar. Biotite is present in considerable quantity as aggregates of orientated granules representing originally coarse plates. Sphene, ilmenite and apatite are common among these aggregates. Hornblende is represented by aggregates of iron ore, biotite, chlorite and sphene. Much of the feldspar is clouded with minute dusky alteration products. Quartz grains are usually surrounded by rims rich in small green biotite crystals. Carbonate and chlorite are accessory.
S.P. 1938 (1940), p. 94.
See also Nos. **642, 679.**

644. Adamellite, ' granodiorite '. Eskdale Granite, post-Borrowdale Volcanic Series (Ordovician), probably Old Red Sandstone. Waberthwaite Quarry, 220 yd S. 15° W. of Bridge End, Waberthwaite, Cumberland. 1-in. 38, 6-in. 82 S.E. (1006. Anal., C. O. Harvey).
cf. E 16732. A grey biotite-adamellite, composed of a hypidiomorphic aggregate of perthitic orthoclase, andesine zoned to oligoclase, and quartz, with plentiful biotite rich in small inclusions of metamict zircon. The biotite is in part altered

B

to chlorite and much of the plagioclase is sericitized. Accessory minerals include garnet, sphene and plentiful apatite.
S.P. 1936, Pt. I (1937), p. 86. *M.G.S.* ' Gosforth ', 1937, p. 128; pl. iii, fig. 6. See also No. **614.**

645. Granodiorite. Practically unfoliated part of Hildasay granitic syenitic mass, ? pre-Old Red Sandstone. ' Later Granite '. Fugla Ness, 440 yd W. 21° S. of pier, Hamnavoe, West Burra, Shetland. 1-in. 126 Scot., 6-in. 56 S.W. (928. Anal., B. E. Dixon).
S 28390. An epidotic granodiorite with large pink phenocrysts of microcline in a groundmass composed of coarse interlocking crystals of oligoclase, quartz which is often granulitized, and microcline, with biotite and much granular yellow epidote. Sphene, ilmenite and apatite are accessory and there is a little interstitial myrmekite. The plagioclase is riddled with white mica, perhaps representing original perthitic intergrowth.
S.P. 1932, Pt. I (1933), p. 96.
See also Nos. **637, 649.**

646. Hornblende-biotite-granodiorite. Injection complex, Shetland Metamorphic Series. Shore S.E. of Mossbank Pier, Delting, Shetland. 1-in. 130 Scot., 6-in. 25 S.E. (1069. Anal., G. A. Sergeant; spect. det., H. K. Whalley).
S 33685. A grey rock composed of hornblende, green and brown biotite, quartz, orthoclase, microcline, oligoclase and common myrmekite. Sphene, epidote and apatite are common as accessories.

	GRANODIORITES			
	645	646	647	648
SiO_2	64·95	64·03	63·70	63·53
Al_2O_3	16·09	15·39	15·10	16·08
Fe_2O_3	2·29	1·25	1·14	1·39
FeO	1·37	2·88	3·10	2·54
MgO	1·37	2·62	2·73	2·58
CaO	3·86	3·74	4·24	4·08
Na_2O	4·28	3·72	4·26	4·64
K_2O	3·90	4·36	3·52	3·43
$H_2O > 105°C$	0·47	0·74	0·30	0·45
$H_2O < 105°C$	0·13	0·15	0·06	0·07
TiO_2	0·70	0·65	1·23	1·14
P_2O_5	0·25	0·34	0·42	0·41
MnO	0·09	0·08	0·07	0·06
CO_2	tr.	tr.	tr.	tr.
Cl	—	tr.	—	—
S	—	tr.	—	—
FeS_2	0·12	—	0·09	0·09
Cr_2O_3	—	0·02	tr.	—
BaO	—	0·16	—	—
SrO	—	0·11(s)	—	—
Rb_2O	—	tr.(s)	—	—
Rare earths	0·03	—	—	—
TOTAL	99·90	100·24	99·96	100·49
Sp. gr.	—	2·68	—	—

647. Microgranodiorite, ' fine-grained dioritic rock '. Probably enclosed in grano- diorite of the Strontian Granite Complex (post-Moine, pre-Middle Old Red Sandstone). Coast, 300 yd W. of Eilean a'Mhuirich, Loch Sunart, Argyllshire. 1-in. 52 Scot., 6-in. 27 S.E. (948. Anal., B. E. Dixon).

S 28456. A grey fine-grained dioritic rock composed of a granular aggregate of quartz, oligoclase and orthoclase, with abundant small prisms of hornblende and tablets of greenish-brown biotite which together sometimes form cumulophyric aggregates. Iron ore, sphene and apatite are plentiful accessories.
S.P. 1933, Pt. I (1934), p. 91.

648. Granodiorite. Member of the Strontian Granite Complex, post-Moine, pre-Middle Old Red Sandstone. Quarry on point 300 yd E.N.E. of Eilean a' Mhuirich, Loch Sunart, Argyllshire. 1-in. 52 Scot., 6-in. 27 S.E. (949. Anal., B. E. Dixon).
S 28738. A grey coarse-grained hornblende-biotite-granodiorite composed of interlocking crystals of oligoclase and quartz and set with pink phenocrysts of microperthite; hornblende and biotite are common and accessory minerals include apatite, opaque ores and plentiful sphene. Chlorite occurs as an alteration product of biotite.
S.P. 1933, Pt. I (1934), p. 91. *Min. Res.*, vol. xxxii, 'Granites of Scotland', 1939, p. 12.
See also Nos. **624, 639, 642.**

649. Granodiorite, 'slightly foliated granite'. Variation of the Hildasay granitic syenitic mass, ? pre-Old Red Sandstone. 'Later Granite'. Shore, St. Mary's Chapel, Sand, Shetland. 1-in. 128 Scot., 6-in. 47 S.E. (969. Anal., C. O. Harvey).
S 30034. A fairly coarse grey granodiorite containing quartz, andesine, oligoclase, microcline, orthoclase, a little myrmekite, biotite, coarse crystals of epidote, usually of irregular outline, and hornblende. Apatite, orthite, sphene and iron ores are present in small quantity and garnet and carbonate are rare

	GRANODIORITE, TONALITE AND QUARTZ-DIORITES			
	649	650	651	652
SiO_2	62·74	61·89	61·64	54·24
Al_2O_3	16·69	14·38	14·56	13·25
Fe_2O_3	1·60	1·67	1·79	0·76
FeO	3·39	8·12	3·75	10·44
MgO	2·54	0·20	4·55	3·63
CaO	5·19	4·54	4·85	6·54
Na_2O	3·22	5·16	4·21	3·38
K_2O	2·75	2·30	1·63	1·18
$H_2O > 105°C$	0·44	0·84	1·42	3·12
$H_2O < 105°C$	0·13	0·30	0·20	0·18
TiO_2	0·64	0·64	0·88	2·40
P_2O_5	0·23	0·14	0·14	0·31
MnO	0·12	0·33	0·10	0·22
CO_2	tr.	tr.	n.d.	0·57
Cl	—	—	—	tr.
S	—	—	0·03	—
FeS_2	0·03	0·07	—	0·14
Fe_7S_8	—	—	—	0·02
Cr_2O_3	0·02	—	0·03	tr.
BaO	0·04	—	0·08	0·02
Rare earths	0·04	—	—	—
Rarer oxides	—	—	0·10(s)*	—
TOTAL	99·81	100·58	99·96	100·40
Sp. gr.	—	—	2·77	2·85 .

* Present in approximately the following percentages:—ZrO_2: 0·02. V_2O_3: 0·01. NiO: 0·01. CoO: <0·004. SrO: 0·06. Ga_2O_3: 0·004. Sc_2O_3: <0·003. Yt_2O_3: <0·01.

accessories. Trains of minute iron ore granules impart a pink colour in hand specimen to the quartz.
S.P. 1934, Pt. I (1935), p. 83.
See also Nos. 637, 645.

650. **Granophyric quartz-diorite.** Carrock Fell Complex, post-Borrowdale Volcanic Series (Ordovician), probably Old Red Sandstone. 690 yd W. 21° S. of Stone Ends, 1 mile N. of Mosedale, Cumberland. 1-in. 23, 6-in. 48 S.W. (943. Anal., B. E. Dixon).
E 16183. A dark-grey rock in which tablets of oligoclase-andesine zoned to albite, stumpy prisms of hedenbergite, opaque ores and much fine-grained chlorite are set in a granophyric matrix of quartz and perthitic orthoclase.
See also Nos. 615, 629, 675, 688, 706, 743-4.

651. **Tonalite.** Near centre of diorite mass that contaminates adjacent Moine Schists. Crags high above forest road, 1830 yd W. 11° S. of mouth of Allt Glas Dhoire Mòr, W. of Loch Lochy, Inverness-shire. 1-in. 62 Scot., 6-in. 111 S.E. (1644. Anal., A. D. Wilson and P. Coombs; spect. det., C. O. Harvey and K. L. H. Murray).
S 40137. A pinkish-grey tonalite composed of andesine zoned to oligoclase, a little microperthite, quartz, abundant hornblende and partly chloritized biotite, with accessory sphene, iron ore, epidote, zircon and apatite.
S.P. 1954 (1955), p. 60.

652. **Quartz-diorite.** Sill-like mass (? Old Red Sandstone) in Skiddaw Slate (Ordovician). Close Quarry, Embleton, 3½ miles E. of Cockermouth, Cumberland. 1-in. 23, 6-in. 55 N.W. (1009. Anal., C. O. Harvey).
E 17423. A medium-grey granophyric diorite composed of turbid tablets of oligoclase, prisms of augite and brown hornblende, ragged flakes of biotite and interstitial quartz and micropegmatite. The oligoclase often contains prehnite aggregates. Iron ore is plentiful and there are numerous prisms of apatite and a little interstitial carbonate.
S.P. 1936, Pt. I (1937), p. 86.

653. **Diorite.** Intrusion, ? Old Red Sandstone. ⅓ mile E.N.E. of Dykes, near Loch of Arg, Sandsting, Shetland. 1-in. 126 Scot., 6-in. 51 N.W. (1066. Anal., G. A. Sergeant; spect. det., H. K. Whalley).
S 33678. A pinkish-grey quartz-rich diorite composed of hornblende, biotite and sphene moulded upon tablets of andesine zoned to oligoclase, and interstitial microperthite, microcline and quartz. Apatite and opaque iron ore including pyrite are accessory.

654. **Hypersthene-diorite.** Intrusion. N.W. shore of Hevden Ness, Delting, Shetland. 1-in. 128 Scot., 6-in. 36 N.E. (1063. Anal., C. O. Harvey; spect. det., H. K. Whalley).
S 33679. A pinkish-grey rock composed of prisms of hypersthene often idiomorphic and sometimes with coronae of amphibole, elongate prisms of augite and tablets of andesine with interstitial orthoclase and a little myrmekite. Biotite is present in subordinate amount and there is a little iron ore.

655. **Diorite.** Intrusion, ? Old Red Sandstone. ¼ mile E.N.E. of Lunga Water, Sandsting, Shetland. 1-in. 125 Scot., 6-in. 51 N.W. (1067. Anal., G. A. Sergeant; spect. det., H. K. Whalley).
S 33676. A pinkish-grey rock composed of an aggregate of andesine tablets zoned to oligoclase, allotriomorphic microcline and quartz, hornblende and biotite moulded upon the feldspar, sphene and accessory apatite and iron ore including pyrite.

656. **Diorite.** Intrusion, ? Old Red Sandstone. 150 yd N.E. of Loch of Arg, Sandsting, Shetland. 1-in. 126 Scot., 6-in. 51 N.W. (1068. Anal., G. A. Sergeant).
S 33677. A grey rock containing bytownite zoned to oligoclase, microcline, a little quartz, abundant hornblende often replaced by biotite, sphene, accessory apatite and opaque iron ore including pyrite, and secondary epidote and prehnite.

	DIORITES			
	653	654	655	656
SiO_2	57·60	56·30	55·35	51·94
Al_2O_3	16·66	14·01	17·82	18·65
Fe_2O_3	2·60	0·71	2·28	1·49
FeO	4·34	5·79	3·86	4·04
MgO	2·99	10·10	3·58	5·86
CaO	5·27	6·73	6·60	8·96
Na_2O	3·97	3·13	4·28	3·18
K_2O	3·01	2·09	2·88	2·24
$H_2O > 105°C$	1·05	0·23	0·76	1·20
$H_2O < 105°C$	0·27	0·15	0·18	0·16
TiO_2	1·73	0·69	1·74	1·34
P_2O_5	0·59	0·15	0·66	0·68
MnO	0·11	0·13	0·13	0·10
CO_2	tr.	tr.	tr.	n.d.
SO_3	—	—	—	tr.
Cl	0·04	—	0·02	tr.
S	0·05	n.d.	0·03	—
FeS_2	—	—	—	0·13
Fe_7S_8	—	—	—	n.d.
Cr_2O_3	—	0·13	—	tr.
BaO	0·12	0·06	0·11	0·09
SrO	—	0·03(s)	—	—
Rb_2O	0·01(s)	—	0·01(s)	—
TOTAL	100·41	100·43	100·29	100·06
Less O for Cl	0·01	—	—	—
	100·40	100·43	100·29	100·06
Sp. gr.	2·79	—	2·78	—

657. Dioritic appinite. Sill in Moine Schists. E. side of Beinn Gàire, 1030 yd N. 25° W. of N. end of Lochan Dubh, Moidart, Inverness-shire. 1-in. 52 Scot., 6-in. 149 N.E. (1018. Anal., C. O. Harvey).
S 31738. A grey member of the appinite suite, composed of hypidiomorphic to allotriomorphic hornblende, well-crystallized biotite sometimes mantled by hornblende, plagioclase tablets zoned from labradorite to oligoclase, and allotriomorphic quartz. Iron ore is common in the hornblende and biotite; apatite is a common accessory.
S.P. 1937 (1938), p. 96.

658. Dioritic appinite. Sill in Moine Schists. Stream, 20 yd from Loch na Bioraich, ¼ mile E. 30° S. of summit of Beinn Gàire, Moidart, Inverness-shire. 1-in. 52 Scot., 6-in. 149 S.W. (977. Anal., B. E. Dixon).
S 30647. A greenish-black member of the appinite suite, composed of abundant coarse prisms of hornblende and numerous small pale-green pyroxene crystals cemented by oligoclase with interstitial quartz. Rare accessories include biotite, sphene and iron ore.

659. Ultrabasic appinite. Sill in Moine Schists. Stream, 200 yd S.W. of S.W. end of Loch na Bioraich, ¼ mile E. 30° S. of summit of Beinn Gàire, Moidart, Inverness-shire. 1-in. 52 Scot., 6-in. 149 S.W. (978. Anal., B. E. Dixon).
S 30648. A greenish-black ultrabasic member of the appinite suite, a phlogopite-bearing harzburgite, composed of abundant olivine poikilitically enclosed by coarse hypersthene, phlogopite in part chloritized and a little pale amphibole. The olivine is partly serpentinized and encloses abundant iron ore.

	APPINITES			TRACHYANDESITES	
	657	658	659	660	661
SiO_2	53·86	52·93	40·77	63·89	60·79
Al_2O_3	15·00	6·17	5·73	14·33	17·86
Fe_2O_3	1·61	1·41	3·62	4·75	2·54
FeO	7·35	5·45	5·98	1·14	2·06
MgO	7·06	16·73	30·90	1·30	2·21
CaO	7·94	13·68	3·83	1·98	3·73
Na_2O	2·43	0·80	0·70	5·85	5·00
K_2O	1·29	1·11	0·58	3·68	3·02
$H_2O>105°C$	1·51	0·21	5·87	0·79	1·39
$H_2O<105°C$	0·13	0·03	0·34	0·52	0·47
TiO_2	1·55	0·72	0·72	1·24	0·69
P_2O_5	0·22	0·04	0·03	0·59	0·49
MnO	0·14	0·21	0·17	0·21	0·11
CO_2	—	tr.	0·33	tr.	tr.
ZrO_2	—	—	\—	—	n.d.(s)
S	0·02	—	—	—	0·02
FeS_2	—	0·03	0·13	0·08	—
Cr_2O_3	0·04	0·28	0·37	—	tr.
V_2O_3	—	—	—	—	n.d.(s)
NiO	—	} tr.	0·06	—	n.d.(s)
CoO	—			—	—
BaO	0·03	—	—	—	0·06
SrO	—	—	—	—	tr.(s)
Li_2O	—	—	—	tr.	—
C	0·01	—	—	—	—
TOTAL	100·19	99·80	100·13	100·35	100·44
Sp. gr.	2·91	—	—	—	2·67

TRACHYANDESITES AND ANDESITES

660. Trachyandesite. Lower Carboniferous lava. Scarp below trigonometrical height 519, S.W. side of Craigmarloch Wood, 1½ miles N.W. of Kilmacolm, Renfrewshire. 1-in. 30 Scot., 6-in. 6 N.E. (918. Anal., B. E. Dixon).
S 28078. A brown trachyandesite composed of phenocrysts of andesine zoned to oligoclase, idiomorphic diopside phenocrysts, usually elongate, and pseudomorphs after olivine in opaque iron ore, chlorite and quartz in an orthophyric groundmass of orthoclase and subordinate oligoclase with granules of iron ore, a few grains of diopside, needles of apatite, biotite and a little chlorite. *S.P.* 1932, Pt. II (1933), p. 88; pl. viii, figs. 1 and 2.
See also No. 704.

661. Trachyandesite. Lower Old Red Sandstone lava. Quarry, 1600 yd E. 31° N. of Ledlanet House, Orwell, Kinross-shire. 1-in. 40 Scot., 6-in. 17 N.E. (1525. Anal., W. F. Waters; spect. det., J. A. C. McClelland).
S 36605. A grey trachyandesite composed of rare small phenocrysts of considerably chloritized oligoclase and occasional coarse limonitized ore crystals set in a trachytic groundmass of laths of oligoclase, abundant granules of ore, chlorite, interstitial orthoclase and andesine.

662. Hornblende-andesite. Lower Old Red Sandstone lava. Old quarry, 800 yd E.S.E. of Middle Third, Dunning, Perthshire. 1-in. 40 Scot., 6-in. 119 N.W. (1524. Anal., W. F. Waters; spect. det., J. A. C. McClelland).

S 36913. A dark-grey hornblende-andesite composed of phenocrysts of hornblende rimmed by magnetite, and andesine with well-developed oscillatory zoning, in a hyalopilitic groundmass of andesine microlites, iron ore granules and devitrified glass.

663. **Augite-andesite.** Lower Old Red Sandstone lava. Waterfall, middle of E. side of site of Humeston Wood, Carrick Hills, 2 miles N.W. of Maybole, Ayrshire. 1-in. 14 Scot., 6-in. 38 N.E. (1004. Anal., C. O. Harvey).
S 27556. A fine-grained dark-grey augite-andesite composed of small phenocrysts of augite, often in glomeroporphyritic aggregates, and andesine zoned to oligoclase in a groundmass of andesine laths showing a tendency to flow texture, ore granules and abundant interstitial brown glass patchily replaced by chlorite. *S.P.* 1936, Pt. I (1937), p. 86. *M.G.S.* ' Central Ayrshire ', 1949, p. 137.

664. **Andesite.** Silurian lava. Moons Hill Quarry, Stoke St. Michael, Somerset. 1-in. 281, 6-in. 42 N.W. (1432. Anal., G. A. Sergeant).
E 20837. A purple epidotized and chloritized quartz-pyroxene-andesite composed of pseudomorphs in chlorite after pyroxene, and aggregates of epidote after feldspar in a groundmass of oligoclase with abundant flakes of chlorite, granules of epidote and iron ore. Very irregular narrow veinlets of granular quartz traverse the rock and quartz also appears to be present in the groundmass. *Min. Res.*, vol. xxxiv, ' Rock Wool ', 2nd edit., 1949, pp. 8, 36.

	ANDESITES				
	662	663	664	665	666
SiO_2 ..	62·09	60·12	57·06	56·28	54·16
Al_2O_3 ..	17·30	16·26	16·32	14·25	19·68
Fe_2O_3 ..	3·74	1·67	4·06	2·38	1·45
FeO	0·92	3·76	1·87	7·36	4·38
MgO ..	2·41	2·52	3·50	2·55	2·90
CaO ..	3·94	5·47	8·26	6·53	8·78
Na_2O ..	4·27	4·17	2·41	2·47	2·46
K_2O ..	2·96	1·19	0·83	2·75	1·45
$H_2O>105°C$	1·10	2·00	3·69	1·69	1·88
$H_2O<105°C$	0·69	1·03	0·66	0·28	0·28
TiO_2 ..	0·65	1·44	0·83	2·65	1·42
P_2O_5 ..	0·39	0·30	0·29	0·48	0·23
MnO ..	0·05	0·12	0·13	0·28	0·09
CO_2	tr.	0·02	n.d.	0·10	0·70
ZrO_2 ..	n.d.(s)	—	—	—	—
Cl	—	—	tr.	—	—
S	0·02	—	0·01	—	—
FeS_2 ..	—	tr.	—	0·11	0·08
Cr_2O_3 ..	tr.	—	0·01	—	—
V_2O_3 ..	n.d.(s)	—	—	—	—
NiO	n.d.(s)	—	—	—	—
BaO ..	0·06	0·04	0·03	—	—
SrO	tr.(s)	—	—	—	—
Li_2O ..	—	—	tr.	—	—
TOTAL	100·59	100·11	99·96	100·16	99·94
Sp. gr. ..	2·68	2·61	2·83	—	—

665. **Andesite.** Lava, Borrowdale Volcanic Series (Ordovician). Top of Binsey, 1466 ft O.D., Cumberland. 1-in. 23, 6-in. 46 N.E. (951. Anal., B. E. Dixon).
E 16234. A dark-grey sparsely porphyritic andesite composed of scarce phenocrysts of andesine or labradorite, albitized and replaced by chlorite, with rare

small augite phenocrysts in a groundmass of andesine laths and small pigeonite crystals cemented by oligoclase. There are abundant ore granules and apatite needles, a little interstitial quartz and accessory carbonate.

666. Andesite. Lava of Eycott type, Borrowdale Volcanic Series (Ordovician). 850 yd S. 30° W. of High Ireby Grange, High Ireby, Cumberland. 1-in. 23, 6-in. 46 N.E. (950. Anal., B. E. Dixon).
E 16233. A dark-grey labradorite-hypersthene-andesite composed of abundant robust idiomorphic phenocrysts of labradorite reaching 2 cm in length and pseudomorphs in chlorite and epidote after hypersthene in a hyalopilitic ground-mass of stout laths of labradorite often 0·1 mm long, granular augite and iron ore with abundant interstitial glass replaced by chlorite. There are rare small amygdales filled with chlorite and microcrystalline quartz.

LAMPROPHYRES

667. Foliated lamprophyre. Foliated edge of 2 ft 6 in. lamprophyre intrusion in Moine Schists. Shore 125 yd E. 13° S. from South Point, Port na h-Uamha, Loch Sunart, Argyllshire. 1-in. 52 Scot., 6-in. 27 N.W. (1627. Anal., A. D. Wilson and P. Coombs; spect. det., C. O. Harvey and K. L. H. Murray).
S 39665. A foliated or schistose grey dioritic lamprophyre, approaching a lamproschist, composed of coarse greenish-brown biotite flakes and finer-grained mainly bluish hornblende prisms orientated in a parallel fashion and spread through a granular groundmass of quartz and oligoclase with accessory sphene. The hornblende sometimes contains fine-grained opaque ore inclusions.
S.P. 1953 (1954), p. 62.
For massive part of lamprophyre see No. **668.**

668. Lamprophyre. Massive part of 2 ft 6 in. lamprophyre intrusion in Moine Schists. Shore 125 yd E. 13° S. from South Point, Port na h-Uamha, Loch Sunart, Argyllshire. 1-in. 52 Scot., 6-in. 27 N.W. (1626. Anal., A. D. Wilson and P. Coombs; spect. det., C. O. Harvey and K. L. H. Murray).
S 39664. A grey dioritic lamprophyre composed of elongate prisms of bluish hornblende and tablets of greenish-brown biotite rather randomly orientated in a base of stumpy prisms of zoned oligoclase interlocked with equidimensional quartz and a little orthoclase. Sphene and opaque ore, mainly pyrite, are plentiful and the hornblende commonly contains fine-grained rod-like ore inclusions. Apatite is a plentiful accessory.
S.P. 1953 (1954), p. 62.
For foliated part of lamprophyre see No. **667.**

669. Lamprophyric inclusion. Representative of large grey inclusion in granodiorite of Strontian Granite Complex (post-Moine, pre-Middle Old Sandstone). Roadside, 670 yd W. of Rudha na Cloiche, Loch Sunart, Argyllshire. 1-in. 52 Scot., 6-in. 28 S.W. (1629. Anal., A. D. Wilson and P. Coombs; spect. det., C. O. Harvey and K. L. H. Murray).
S 39667. A mottled fine-grained pink-speckled grey dioritic lamprophyre com-posed of small robust hornblende prisms and biotite tablets in a base of tabular oligoclase, sometimes sericitized, and subordinate orthoclase. Abundant small needles of apatite, crystals of sphene and a little carbonate are accessory.
S.P. 1953 (1954), p. 62.

670. Lamprophyre. 2 ft 6 in. sheet cutting injected pelitic Moine schist. Roadside, 1030 yd E. 42° S. of Inn, Salen, Loch Sunart, Argyllshire. 1-in. 52 Scot., 6-in. 26 N.E. (1628. Anal., A. D. Wilson and P. Coombs; spect. det., C. O. Harvey and K. L. H. Murray).
S 39666. A coarse grey biotite-bearing spessartite composed of ragged prisms of bluish-green hornblende and flakes of biotite, often in aggregates with horn-blende, cemented by tabular oligoclase with plentiful interstitial granulitized oligoclase and albite and scarce orthoclase. The tabular feldspar is often turbid

	LAMPROPHYRES			
	667	668	669	670
SiO₂..	57·90	53·86	52·84	49·00
Al₂O₃	16·00	16·30	17·84	11·68
Fe₂O₃	1·53	2·19	1·63	2·24
FeO..	4·10	4·40	4·82	7·34
MgO	5·75	6·54	5·55	10·62
CaO..	5·58	7·96	5·51	10·14
Na₂O	4·29	4·13	5·15	2·90
K₂O..	1·93	1·31	2·30	0·79
H₂O>105°C	0·95	1·31	1·74	2·05
H₂O<105°C	0·17	0·25	0·27	0·30
TiO₂	1·00	1·20	1·48	1·24
P₂O₅	0·26	0·24	0·52	0·23
MnO	0·09	0·09	0·12	0·19
CO₂..	n.d.	n.d.	0·23	0·81
SO₃..	n.d.	n.d.	—	n.d.
Cl	tr.	tr.	tr.	tr.
FeS₂..	0·11*	0·24*	0·06*	0·22*
Cr₂O₃	0·02	0·03	0·02	0·09
BaO..	0·09	0·06	0·04	0·04
Li₂O	0·0027(s)	0·0020(s)	0·0044(s)	0·0039(s)
Rb₂O	0·0058(s)	0·0032(s)	0·0075(s)	0·0011(s)
Cs₂O	n.d. (<0·02; s)	n.d. (<0·02; s)	n.d. (<0·02; s)	n.d. (<0·01; s)
TOTAL	99·77	100·11	100·13	99·88
Sp. gr.	2·80	2·85	2·81	2·97

* S calculated as FeS₂.

with alteration products. Granules and idiomorphic crystals of sphene and needles of apatite are plentiful; a little pyrite and coarse carbonate are also present.
S.P. 1953 (1954), p. 62.

671. Biotite-camptonite. Dyke cutting Old Red Sandstone. Shore of Loch of Skaill, Sandwick, Orkney. 1-in. 119 Scot., 6-in. 94 S.W. (911. Anal., B. E. Dixon). S 27538. A feldspathic biotite-camptonite containing idiomorphic phenocrysts of green pyroxene, occasional pseudomorphs in chlorite and carbonate, and scarce brown hornblende crystals surrounded by secondary outgrowths of deep-blue amphibole. The groundmass is composed of abundant small crystals of iron ore, biotite and pyroxene and irregularly arranged tabular prisms of rather turbid feldspar which is mainly oligoclase with some orthoclase. There are numerous interstitial patches of chlorite, abundant needles of apatite and irregular crystals of carbonate.
S.P. 1931, Pt. I (1932), p. 79. M.G.S. ' Orkneys ', 1935, p. 178; pl. viii, fig. 2.

672. Camptonite. Dyke cutting Moine Schists. Coast 320 yd S.E. of Rhuda Àird Earnaich, Loch Sunart, Argyllshire. 1-in. 52 Scot., 6-in. 26 N.E. (1070. Anal., G. A. Sergeant; spect. det., H. K. Whalley). S 32739. A dark-grey rock in which there are scarce serpentinous pseudomorphs after originally idiomorphic olivine. The groundmass is composed of prisms of pale-purple pyroxene, brown hornblende often mantling the pyroxene, crystals of iron ore and tablets of biotite with coarse laths of andesine zoned to oligoclase. Apatite needles are plentiful. Analcite and carbonate are present interstitially and in small ocelli.

	CAMPTONITES			
	671	672	673	674
SiO_2 ..	46·85	43·91	43·03	42·38
Al_2O_3	12·86	14·72	10·07	14·79
Fe_2O_3	3·81	4·19	4·36	4·91
FeO ..	8·07	6·79	7·55	7·00
MgO	6·10	7·11	8·46	5·47
CaO ..	5·67	10·85	10·42	9·47
Na_2O	4·91	3·25	2·47	4·00
K_2O ..	2·30	1·69	1·60	2·78
$H_2O > 105°C$	2·30	2·08	1·89	2·30
$H_2O < 105°C$	1·47	0·47	1·75	0·23
TiO_2	3·35	2·09	3·19	2·97
P_2O_5	0·78	0·62	0·57	1·36
MnO	—	0·17	—	0·20
CO_2 ..	1·31	1·66	4·09	1·26
SO_3 ..	—	tr.	—	tr.
Cl	—	tr.	—	tr.
F	—	tr.	—	tr.
FeS_2 ..	0·39	0·32	0·18	0·34
Fe_7S_8	—	tr.	—	tr.
Cr_2O_3	—	0·02	0·20	tr.
NiO ⎫ CoO ⎬	0·06	—	—	—
BaO ..	—	0·08	—	0·15
SrO ..	—	0·09(s)	—	0·10(s)
Li_2O	—	tr.	—	tr.
TOTAL	100·23	100·11	99·83	99·71
Sp. gr.	—	2·91	—	2·92

673. Camptonite. Dyke cutting Old Red Sandstone. Shore of Loch of Skaill, Sandwick, Orkney. 1-in. 119 Scot., 6-in. 94 S.W. (913. Anal., B. E. Dixon).
S 27537. Numerous idiomorphic olivine phenocrysts, often several millimetres in length and entirely altered to serpentine and carbonate, are set in a groundmass of small purplish-brown prisms of augite, abundant robust small prisms of brown hornblende, crystals of iron ore and laths of andesine zoned to oligoclase. There are numerous slender needles of apatite and chlorite is a common alteration product. Scarce patches of carbonate, chlorite and quartz may represent steam-cavities.
S.P. 1931, Pt. I (1932), p. 79. *M.G.S.* ' Orkneys ', 1935, p. 177.

674. Camptonite. Dyke cutting Strontian Granite Complex (post-Moine, pre-Middle Old Red Sandstone). Allt Fèith Mhic Artair, 230 yd N.W. of junction with Allt na h-Easaiche, Kingairloch, Argyllshire. 1-in. 52 Scot., 6-in. 56 S.W. (1071. Anal., G. A. Sergeant; spect. det., H. K. Whalley).
S 32743. A dark-grey camptonite in which the phenocrysts consist of idiomorphic brown zoned hornblende and scarce greenish pyroxene. The groundmass is composed of small hornblende prisms, iron ore crystals, pyroxene prisms, carbonate and needles of apatite with coarse clear laths of andesine zoned to oligoclase enclosing the other minerals. Turbid patches of the matrix are probably in part analcite.

QUARTZ-GABBRO AND QUARTZ-DOLERITES

675. Quartz-gabbro. Carrock Fell Complex, post-Borrowdale Volcanic Series (Ordovician), probably Old Red Sandstone. 920 yd N. 39° W. of Mosedale Bridge over River Caldew, Mosedale, Cumberland. 1-in. 23, 6-in. 48 S.W. (941. Anal., B. E. Dixon).

E 16181. A coarse mottled greenish-grey and white rock containing hypidio-morphic tablets of zoned labradorite often sericitized, irregular crystals of augite with closely spaced cleavage moulded upon feldspar and replaced by hornblende, and quartz graphically intergrown with feldspar. Ilmenite forms coarse plates and there is a little biotite. Chlorite is extensively developed. See also Nos. **615, 629, 650, 688, 706, 743-4.**

676. **Quartz-dolerite,** feldspathic. Sill in rocks of Carboniferous Limestone Series. Central portion of Auchinbee Quarry, Croy, Dumbartonshire. 1-in. 31 Scot., 6-in. 29 S.W. (1431. Anal., G. A. Sergeant).
S 32450. A light-grey feldspathic modification of quartz-dolerite, composed of well-formed tablets of oligoclase, ragged hornblende prisms, augite, enstatite, interstitial quartz and interstitial micropegmatite which is mainly very fine-grained. Hornblende and pyroxene are partly altered to iron ore and chlorite. Carbonate and apatite are accessory.

677. **Quartz-dolerite.** Near middle of sill in rocks of Carboniferous Limestone Series. 1442 ft deep, Rashiehill Borehole, near Slamannan, Stirlingshire. 1-in. 31 Scot., 6-in. 35 N.W. (1640. Anal., A. D. Wilson and P. Coombs; spect. det., C. O. Harvey and K. L. H. Murray).

	QUARTZ-GABBRO AND QUARTZ-DOLERITES				
	675	676	677	678	679
SiO_2 ..	52·25	59·15	53·05	52·12	51·44
Al_2O_3 ..	18·71	13·46	12·01	14·59	14·39
Fe_2O_3 ..	0·90	1·79	4·07	3·08	1·66
FeO ..	7·86	7·23	8·47	6·82	8·91
MgO ..	2·84	2·06	3·94	5·88	7·76
CaO ..	9·52	4·32	6·52	9·14	9·52
Na_2O ..	2·90	4·22	3·05	2·92	2·73
K_2O ..	1·18	2·50	1·39	0·58	0·41
$H_2O > 105°C$	1·15	1·83	1·87	0·88	0·90
$H_2O < 105°C$	0·16	0·36	1·24	1·34	0·55
TiO_2 ..	2·18	1·84	2·99	1·55	1·57
P_2O_5 ..	0·30	0·64	0·45	0·18	0·19
MnO ..	0·17	0·18	0·18	0·17	0·16
CO_2	—	0·22	0·86	0·62	tr.
SO_3	—	—	n.d.	—	—
Cl	—	tr.	—	—	—
S	—	0·02	—	—	—
FeS_2 ..	0·02	—	0·19*	0·15	0·05
Fe_7S_8 ..	—	—	—	tr.	0·03
Cr_2O_3 ..	—	n.d.	tr.	0·01	0·05
NiO ..	—	—	—	—	} 0·02
CoO ..	—	—	—	—	
BaO ..	—	0·08	0·03	0·02	—
Li_2O ..	—	—	0·001(s)†	—	—
Rb_2O ..	—	—	0·002(s)†	—	—
Cs_2O ..	—	—	n.d. (<0·01; s)	—	—
TOTAL	100·14 -	99·90	100·31‡	100·05	100·34
Sp. gr. ..	—	2·78	2·83	2·83	2·94

* Total S calculated as FeS_2.
† Approximate.
‡ Approximate percentages (s):—Ga: 0·002. Ni: n.d. (<0·001). Sr: 0·03. V: 0·03. Yt: 0·01. Zr: 0·02.

S 39366. A coarse pinkish-grey albitized micropegmatitic quartz-dolerite composed of strongly zoned plagioclase laths up to 4 mm in length in a groundmass
of fine-grained micropegmatite and quartz. Augite prisms are largely replaced
by turbid chlorite, sphene, leucoxene and opaque ore which also occurs in
separate granules. Apatite needles are plentiful; coarse carbonate is moulded
upon feldspar.
S.P. 1953 (1954), p. 63.
See also Nos. **680, 682.**

678. Quartz-dolerite. Boss intruded into Moine Schists; probably Permo-Carboniferous. Shore at Morroch Point, Arisaig, Inverness-shire. 1-in. 61 Scot.,
6-in. 120 S.E. (1052. Anal., C. O. Harvey).
S 32738. A coarse rock containing laths and tablets of labradorite zoned to
oligoclase, augite moulded upon the feldspar, opaque iron ore including rare
pyrite, chloritic decomposition products and interstitial quartz and abundant
micropegmatite.

679. Olivine-bearing quartz-dolerite. Boss in tonalite of Strontian Granite Complex
(post-Moine, pre-Middle Old Red Sandstone); probably Permo-Carboniferous.
1300 yd N. 20° W. of Longrigg, near Strontian, Argyllshire. 1-in. 52 Scot.,
6-in. 27 N.E. (1041. Anal., C. O. Harvey).
S 30207. A dark-grey rock in which olivine phenocrysts, represented by pseudomorphs in bowlingite, are set among a plexus of labradorite laths on which are
moulded prisms of augite and iron ore. Quartz and micropegmatite are interstitial.
S.P. 1938 (1940), p. 94.
See also No. **643.**

680. Quartz-dolerite. Near top of sill in rocks of Carboniferous Limestone Series.
1366 ft deep, Rashiehill Borehole, near Slamannan, Stirlingshire. 1-in. 31 Scot.,
6-in. 35 N.W. (1639. Anal., A. D. Wilson and P. Coombs; spect. det., C. O.
Harvey and K. L. H. Murray).
S 39360. A grey quartz-dolerite of medium grain size. Prisms of augite are
ophitically moulded upon laths of labradorite zoned to albite. Quartz and
micropegmatite are common interstitially and iron ore and chlorite are plentiful.
A little leucoxene and carbonate are present and there are numerous slender
needles of apatite.
S.P. 1953 (1954), p. 63.
See also Nos. **677, 682.**

681. Quartz-dolerite. Sill in Carboniferous rocks. Braehead Quarry, Four Mile Hill,
Turnhouse, Midlothian. 1-in. 32 Scot., 6-in. 2 N.E. (1430. Anal., G. A.
Sergeant).
S 32449. A fairly coarse dark-grey rock composed of labradorite zoned to
oligoclase and considerably altered to fine-grained white mica, plentiful augite
and hypersthene moulded upon feldspar, and interstitial iron-stained chlorite
and quartz. Allotriomorphic iron ore including pyrite is common.

682. Quartz-dolerite. Near base of sill in rocks of Carboniferous Limestone Series.
1597 ft deep, Rashiehill Borehole, near Slamannan, Stirlingshire. 1-in. 31 Scot.,
6-in. 35 N.W. (1638. Anal., A. D. Wilson and P. Coombs; spect. det., C. O.
Harvey and K. L. H. Murray).
S 39569. A mottled dark-grey pyroxene-rich quartz-dolerite composed of
abundant augite and common hypersthene prisms both ophitically enclosing
labradorite zoned to oligoclase, with interstitial quartz, micropegmatite and
rare alkali-feldspar. Opaque iron ore and chloritic alteration products are
common, and there are numerous small biotite tablets, sphene granules, and
apatite prisms.
S.P. 1953 (1954), p. 63.
See also Nos. **677, 680.**

683. Altered quartz-dolerite. Channel sample 0-5 ft from hanging wall of Winterhush
Vein (barytes) in the Whin Sill (Permo-Carboniferous). 106-ft level, 35 yd N.
of Wrentnall Shaft, Cowgreen Mine, West Common, Co. Durham. 1-in. 25,
6-in. 30 S.W. (1328. Anal., G. A. Sergeant; spect. det., J. A. C. McClelland).
E 20065. A nearly white altered quartz-dolerite retaining its igneous texture.

Ferromagnesian silicates are replaced by calcite and dolomite, the cores of the plagioclase crystals by kaolinite, and iron ores by leucoxene. There is a little micropegmatite, and quartz is common. There are occasional grains of sphalerite.
M.G.S. ' N. Pennine Orefield ', vol. i, 1948, p. 104.

684. **Altered quartz-dolerite.** Channel sample 0-6 ft from hanging wall of Settlingstones Vein (witherite, lead ore) in the Whin Sill (Permo-Carboniferous) 90-fathoms level, 235 yd S.W. of Frederick Shaft, Settlingstones Mine, Newbrough, Northumberland. 1-in. 13, 6-in. 84 S.E. (1327. Anal., G. A. Sergeant; spect. det., J. A. C. McClelland).
E 20064. A nearly white altered quartz-dolerite retaining its igneous texture. Ferromagnesian silicates have been replaced by calcite and dolomite, feldspar by kaolinite and iron ore by leucoxene. Quartz, apatite, alkali-feldspar and pyrite are present in small quantity.
M.G.S. ' N. Pennine Orefield ', vol. i, 1948, p. 104.

	QUARTZ-DOLERITES				
	680	681	682	683	684
SiO_2 ..	50·22	49·69	49·21	40·50	36·78
Al_2O_3 ..	13·22	13·77	14·04	14·98	16·24
Fe_2O_3 ..	2·88	3·75	3·61	0·14§	0·07
FeO.. ..	9·67	7·80	7·69	2·42§	2·71
MgO ..	5·33	5·99	7·11	5·43	0·39
CaO ..	8·91	8·52	10·08	10·54	17·08
Na_2O ..	2·63	3·01	2·71	1·13	0·71
K_2O ..	0·85	1·01	0·78	2·17	1·81
$H_2O > 105°C$	1·75	1·89	1·32	3·92	4·83
$H_2O < 105°C$	1·00	1·45	1·08	0·84	0·55
TiO_2 ..	2·62	2·23	1·83	2·67	2·87
P_2O_5 ..	0·29	0·27	0·19	0·29	0·32
MnO ..	0·15	0·17	0·16	0·36	0·28
CO_2.. ..	0·46	tr.	0·09	14·72	14·75
SO_3	n.d.	0·03	n.d.	tr.	0·06
Cl	—	tr.	—	tr.	tr.
S	—	—	—	0·25	—
FeS_2 ..	0·32*	0·40	0·26*	—	0·63
Fe_7S_8 ..	—	n.d.	—	—	tr.
Cr_2O_3 ..	0·01	0·01	0·01	0·01	0·01
BaO ..	0·01	0·03	0·02	0·06	0·18
SrO	—	—	—	0·02(s)	0·05(s)
PbO	—	—	—	0·02(s)	—
ZnO	—	—	—	0·2(s)	—
Li_2O ..	0·0011(s)	—	0·0012(s)	tr.	tr.
Rb_2O ..	0·0026(s)	—	0·0022(s)	—	—
Cs_2O ..	n.d. (<0·01; s)	—	n.d. (<0·01; s)	—	—
TOTAL	100·32†	100·02	100·20‡	100·67	100·32
Less O for S	—	—	—	0·12	—
	100·32	100·02	100·20	100·55	100·32
Sp. gr. ..	2·90	2·90	2·96	—	—

* Total S calculated as FeS_2.
† Approximate percentages (s):—Ga: 0·002. Ni: 0·004. Sr: 0·03. V: 0·03. Yt: 0·01. Zr: 0·02.
‡ Approximate percentages (s):—Ga: 0·001. Ni: 0·01. Sr: 0·03. V: 0·03. Yt: 0·01.
§ Approximate.

GABBROS

685. Hornblende-gabbro. Variation of dioritic intrusion, ? Old Red Sandstone. Hillside, 150 yd N.E. of the Loch of Arg, Sandsting, Shetland. 1-in. 126 Scot., 6-in. 51 N.W. (970. Anal., B. E. Dixon).
S 30035. A grey rock composed of an aggregate of plagioclase tablets zoned from labradorite to albite, hypidiomorphic prisms of hornblende, and large irregular crystals of chloritized biotite ophitically moulded upon plagioclase. Microcline is interstitial. Coarse granular epidote and robust prisms of apatite are common and coarse pyrite and fine-grained sphene are present in small amount.
S.P. 1934, Pt. I (1935), p. 83.

686. Gabbro. Intrusion, Ballantrae Igneous Complex, Ordovician. Summit of Mains Hill, 600 yd S.E. of Ardmillan House, 2½ miles S.S.W. of Girvan, Ayrshire. 1-in. 7 Scot., 6-in. 55 S.E. (905. Anal., B. E. Dixon).
S 27366. A grey rock composed of hypidiomorphic tablets of saussuritized plagioclase now largely converted to oligoclase, coarse ragged hornblende prisms poikilitically enclosing colourless pyroxene and moulded upon the feldspar, and plates of ilmenite. Veinlets of prehnite traverse the rock.
S.P. 1931, Pt. I (1932), p. 79.
See also Nos. **618, 696, 710, 728.**

	GABBROS			
	685	686	687	688
SiO_2 ..	51·98	45·80	44·95	41·38
Al_2O_3	18·70	16·34	24·02	14·04
Fe_2O_3	1·62	1·67	0·93	3·14
FeO ..	3·95	12·53	4·07	15·90
MgO	5·94	5·39	9·43	5·63
CaO ..	8·88	8·44	13·70	9·73
Na_2O	3·20	3·11	1·21	1·56
K_2O ..	2·27	0·73	0·11	0·72
$H_2O > 105°C$	0·86	2·03	1·27	1·88
$H_2O < 105°C$	0·18	0·23	0·48	0·18
TiO_2	1·36	3·02	0·13	5·05
P_2O_5	0·66	0·10	0·02	0·14
MnO	0·07	—	0·08	0·37
CO_2 ..	—	tr.	tr.	—
S ..	—	—	0·01	—
FeS_2 ..	0·24	0·50	—	0·22
Cr_2O_3	0·03	—	0·05	—
NiO ..	—	—	0·01	—
BaO ..	—	—	0·01	—
SrO ..	—	—	0·02(s)	—
Li_2O	—	—	n.d.	—
TOTAL ..	99·94	99·89	100·50	99·94
Sp. gr. ..	—	—	2·85	—

687. Olivine-gabbro. Boss in Tertiary mugearite; Tertiary. Broisgillmore Burn, ¼ mile S.S.W. of summit of Am Bidean, 2 miles N.N.W. of Bracadale, Skye, Inverness-shire. 1-in. 80 Scot., 6-in. 28 N.E. (1576. Anal., W. F. Waters and K. L. H. Murray).

S 37870. A dark-grey fresh ophitic olivine-gabbro composed of a coarse hypidiomorphic aggregate of labradorite prisms on which augite is ophitically moulded. Rounded olivine crystals, altered marginally to serpentine, are plentiful and are often mantled by the augite. Iron ore is accessory.

688. Ilmenite-gabbro. Carrock Fell Complex, post-Borrowdale Volcanic Series (Ordovician), probably Old Red Sandstone. 600 yd N. 28° W. of Mosedale Bridge over River Caldew, Mosedale, Cumberland. 1-in. 23, 6-in. 48 S.W. (940. Anal., B. E. Dixon).
E 16180. A dark-grey rock composed of a hypidiomorphic aggregate of robust labradorite prisms on which augite and biotite are ophitically moulded, and coarse-grained ilmenite which is sometimes intergrown with magnetite. The augite is partly replaced by hornblende and there is accessory apatite. Chloritic and serpentinous alteration products are common.
See also Nos. **615, 629, 650, 675, 706, 743-4.**

DOLERITES AND BASALTS

689. Olivine-basalt. Lower Old Red Sandstone lava. Old quarry, 1000 yd S. of Finderlie, Orwell, Kinross-shire. 1-in. 40 Scot., 6-in. 18 S.W. (1526. Anal., W. F. Waters; spect. det., J. A. C. McClelland).
S 37266. A grey olivine-basalt. Pseudomorphs in iddingsite and iron ore after olivine are set in a fine-grained base of labradorite laths, pyroxene granules and iron ore, with interstitial alkali-feldspar, chlorite and glass.

690. Olivine-basalt. Lower Old Red Sandstone lava. Old quarry, 200 yd N.W. of Letham House, 1 mile N.E. of Arngask, Perthshire. 1-in. 40 Scot., 6-in. 120 N.E. (1523. Anal., W. F. Waters; spect. det., J. A. C. McClelland).
S 37263. A grey olivine-basalt containing labradorite phenocrysts, sometimes zoned, augite and pseudomorphs in bowlingite and ore after olivine in a groundmass of labradorite laths zoned to oligoclase, granular augite and opaque ore. Interstitial chlorite is present in small quantity and there are abundant small needles of apatite. The rock displays a well-developed flow texture.

691. Dolerite, ' diabase '. Triassic. Bull Run Quarry, U.S. Highway 211, 3¼ miles S.W. of Centerville, Fairfax County, Virginia, United States of America. (1543. Anal., W. F. Waters and P. Coombs; spect. det., C. O. Harvey).
A fresh dolerite composed of labradorite and augite, with small amounts of potash-feldspar, biotite, opaque minerals and quartz.
This rock was analysed as part of the investigation sponsored by various American institutions into the precision and accuracy in chemical, spectrographical and modal analyses of silicate rocks.
Bull. U.S. Geol. Surv., No. 980, 1951, p. 11. ' *Quantitative spectrochemical analysis of silicates* ', L. H. Ahrens, 1954, p. 23. London.

692. Olivine-basalt. Lower Old Red Sandstone lava. Old quarry beside road, 640 yd E.N.E. of Leden Urquhart, 2½ miles E. of Arngask, Perthshire. 1-in. 40 Scot., 6-in. 120 N.E. (1521. Anal., W. F. Waters; spect. det., J. A. C. McClelland).
S 36411. A brownish-grey rock composed of plentiful phenocrysts of labradorite and augite and pseudomorphs after olivine in opaque ore, bowlingite and iddingsite in a groundmass of robust laths of labradorite between which there are granules of augite and iron ore and a mesostasis of chlorite. There are occasional irregular patches of calcite.

693. Olivine-basalt. Lower Old Red Sandstone lava. West bank of burn, 750 yd upstream from High Pinmore, Carrick Hills, Ayrshire. 1-in. 14 Scot., 6-in. 39 N.W. (1003. Anal., C. O. Harvey).
S 31603-4. A porphyritic olivine-basalt containing abundant phenocrysts of labradorite zoned to andesine, with pseudomorphs in serpentinous minerals, iddingsite, carbonate and ore after olivine in a groundmass of labradorite laths

	DOLERITE AND BASALTS				
	689	690	691	692	693
SiO_2 ..	55·84	53·13	52·43	52·28	51·60
Al_2O_3 ..	16·13	17·95	14·86	17·65	17·15
Fe_2O_3 ..	4·66	4·65	1·57	3·69	4·51
FeO	1·78	2·32	8·67	2·56	2·86
MgO ..	4·45	4·06	6·70	4·98	5·11
CaO ..	7·04	7·32	10·91	8·86	7·28
Na_2O ..	3·93	4·35	2·41*	3·73	3·65
K_2O ..	1·93	1·78	0·67	1·30	1·51
$H_2O > 105°C$	1·02	0·71	0·56	1·00	1·45
$H_2O < 105°C$	1·67	1·74	0·16	2·11	2·81
TiO_2 ..	1·15	1·24	1·13	1·21	1·59
P_2O_5 ..	0·29	0·44	0·11	0·31	0·29
MnO ..	0·07	0·20	0·17	0·10	0·09
CO_2	0·33	0·12	—	0·53	0·36
ZrO_2 · ..	n.d.(s)	—	—	—	—
S	0·01	0·02	0·03	0·01	—
FeS_2	—	—	—	—	tr.
Cr_2O_3 ..	0·02	0·01	0·02	0·01	—
V_2O_3 ..	tr.(s)	tr.(s)	—	tr.(s)	—
NiO	tr.(s)	tr.(s)	—	tr.(s)	—
BaO ..	0·05	0·04	0·02	0·03	0·04
SrO	tr.(s)	tr.(s)	—	tr.(s)	—
TOTAL	100·37	100·08	100·42*†	100·36	100·30
Less O for S	—	—	0·01	—	—
	100·37	100·08	100·41	100·36	100·30
Sp. gr. ..	2·70	2·72	—	2·71	2·67

* Amended figures.
† Semi-quantitative percentages (s):—Co: 0·003. Ga: 0·002. Ni: 0·01. Sc: 0·007. Sr: 0·02.
V: 0·03. Yt: 0·003. Zr: 0·01.

upon which abundant small crystals of augite are moulded. Iron ore crystals are common and there are numerous needles of apatite. Some chloritic pseudomorphs may represent orthopyroxene.
S.P. 1936, Pt. I (1937), p. 86. *M.G.S.* ' Central Ayrshire ', 1949, p. 137.

694. Olivine-basalt. Lower Old Red Sandstone lava. 50 yd S. of track, 380 yd E. of Balvaird Farm, 2½ miles E.N.E. of Arngask, Perthshire. 1-in. 40 Scot., 6-in. 120 N.E. (1527. Anal., W. F. Waters; spect. det., J. A. C. McClelland).
S 37267. A grey olivine-basalt containing abundant labradorite phenocrysts, up to about ½ cm in length, mainly arranged in a parallel fashion and set in a fine-grained groundmass made up of small labradorite laths and iron ore granules, apparently mainly haematite. Iron ore crystals up to about 1 mm across in part represent original ferromagnesian minerals. Irregular veinlets of calcite traverse the rock.

695. Olivine-basalt, Crawton type. Lower Old Red Sandstone lava. Base of cliffs, 330 yd E. of Crawton, 4 miles S. of Stonehaven, Kincardineshire. 1-in. 67 Scot., 6-in. 21 S.W. (979. Anal., C. O. Harvey).
S 30692. A brownish-grey olivine-basalt rich in platy phenocrysts of labradorite which reach about 3 cm in length and are arranged in a parallel fashion. Olivine phenocrysts are represented by pseudomorphs in ore and carbonate. The groundmass is composed of small laths of labradorite with granules of

pale augite, plentiful iron ore, including haematite, in grains and aggregates, abundant needles of apatite and interstitial oligoclase. The rock is traversed by irregular veinlets of calcite.

696. **Tachylyte.** Blocks in agglomerate of Ballantrae Igneous Complex, Ordovician. Slockenray Bay, 1¼ miles N.N.E. of Lendalfoot, Ayrshire. 1-in. 7 Scot., 6-in. 61 N.W. (908. Anal., B. E. Dixon).
S 27370. A brownish porphyritic tachylyte having a resinous lustre. The rock is composed of numerous labradorite phenocrysts, sometimes a centimetre in length, in a base of labradorite laths mainly less than 0·15 mm, long, abundant granules of titanaugite and abundant interstitial chloritic matter and iron ore. Apatite is accessory.
S.P. 1931, Pt. I (1932), p. 79. *Geol. Mag.*, vol. lxix, 1932, p. 111; pl. vi, fig. 4.
See also Nos. **618, 686, 710, 728.**

	DOLERITE AND BASALTS				
	694	695	696	697	698
SiO_2	51·11	50·75	47·01	45·99	45·71
Al_2O_3	17·61	17·01	18·07	14·65	14·53
Fe_2O_3	8·29	9·31	5·15	2·23	4·24
FeO	0·33	0·72	5·20	9·80	7·31
MgO	2·55	2·20	3·17	9·46	8·72
CaO	7·50	7·25	10·00	8·68	7·41
Na_2O	4·17	4·20	3·46	2·83	2·97
K_2O	1·94	2·34	0·63	0·46	0·63
$H_2O > 105°C$	1·19	1·15	1·11	2·34	3·40
$H_2O < 105°C$	1·44	1·16	2·38	1·38	3·01
TiO_2	1·68	2·34	2·94	1·90	1·49
P_2O_5	0·43	0·78	0·45	0·20	0·30
MnO	0·11	0·08	0·10	0·19	0·13
CO_2	2·02	1·09	0·16	tr.	0·35
ZrO_2	n.d.(s)	—	—	—	—
SO_3	—	—	—	—	tr.
Cl	—	0·02	—	—	tr.
S	0·01	—	—	0·02	0·04
FeS_2	—	0·08	0·14	—	—
Cr_2O_3	n.d.	tr.	—	0·05	0·07
V_2O_3	tr.(s)	—	—	—	n.d.(s)
NiO	tr.(s)	—	—	0·01	tr.(s)
CoO	—	—	—	—	tr.(s)
BaO	0·05	0·05	—	0·01	0·02(s)
SrO	tr.(s)	—	—	0·03(s)	0·03(s)
Li_2O	—	—	n.d.	n.d.	n.d.
Pt	—	—	—	—	n.d.(s)
TOTAL	100·43	100·53	99·97	100·23	100·36
Sp. gr.	2·71	—	—	2·90	—

697. **Olivine-basalt.** Tertiary lava. Creag Mhòr, cliff W. of Beal Point, Rudha na h-Àirde Glaise, Skye, Inverness-shire. 1-in. 81 Scot., 6-in. 24 S.W. (1577. Anal., W. F. Waters).
S 37873. A dark-grey olivine-basalt containing idiomorphic olivine phenocrysts and bowlingitic pseudomorphs after olivine in a base of labradorite laths. Augite is abundant as large irregular crystals ophitically moulded upon the feldspar. There is much interstitial chlorite, and opaque ore is common.

C

698. Olivine-dolerite. Sill intruded near base of Coal Measures. 2343 ft deep, Knap-
thorpe Borehole No. G. 1, 5 miles N.W. of Newark-upon-Trent, Nottinghamshire. 1-in. 113, 6-in. 30 N.W. (1477. Anal., C. O. Harvey; spect. det., J. A. C.
McClelland).

E 21662. A dark-grey ophitic olivine-dolerite composed of pseudomorphs in
microcrystalline serpentinous alteration products and carbonate after olivine,
and coarse-grained titanaugite moulded upon labradorite laths which are often
a millimetre in length. Opaque iron ores and idiomorphic crystals of sphene
are common. Interstitial chlorite, often having a spherulitic texture, is present
in considerable quantity.

699. Olivine-basalt. Tertiary lava. Creag Mhòr, cliff W. of Beal Point, Rudha na
h-Àirde Glaise, Skye, Inverness-shire. 1-in. 81 Scot., 6-in. 24 S.W. (1578.
Anal., W. F. Waters and K. L. H. Murray).

S 37874. An amygdaloidal chloritized olivine-basalt. Feldspar has been extensively replaced by chlorite and original ferromagnesian minerals by iron ore.
Numerous amygdales, up to several millimetres across, contain analcite
bordered by radiating tufts of stilbite. Chloritic minerals are frequently present
in the amygdales.

	BASALTS			PALAGO-NITE-TUFF	MUGEARITES	
	699	700	701	702	703	704
SiO_2 ..	42·40	42·30	34·27	33·24	48·12	48·04
Al_2O_3 ..	14·66	14·24	19·72	21·53	16·30	14·93
Fe_2O_3 ..	8·82	3·87	18·55	3·23*	4·90	12·16
FeO ..	4·92	5·49	0·82	—	9·11	2·33
MgO ..	8·33	4·42	5·05	0·72	3·80	3·45
CaO ..	8·40	16·76	6·48	2·36	5·97	6·81
Na_2O ..	2·60	2·40	1·70	0·13	5·69	4·74
K_2O ..	0·30	0·27	0·32	0·07	0·74	1·94
$H_2O > 105°C$	3·68	1·22	6·31	—	1·01	1·00
$H_2O < 105°C$	3·76	1·69	3·51	—	0·77	0·95
TiO_2 ..	2·09	1·57	2·71	2·73	2·74	3·50
P_2O_5 ..	0·21	0·18	0·20	0·25	0·56	0·55
MnO ..	0·15	0·24	0·20	0·09	0·20	0·14
CO_2 ..	tr.	5·07	0·01	—	n.d.	tr.
Cl	—	—	—	tr.	—	—
S ..	0·01	0·09	tr.	n.d.	tr.	—
FeS_2 ..	—	—	—	—	—	0·04
Cr_2O_3 ..	0·03	0·04	0·03	tr.	tr.	—
NiO ..	0·01	—	0·02	—	tr.	—
BaO ..	0·01	0·07	0·01	0·10	0·02	—
SrO	0·03(s)	—	0·07(s)	—	0·05(s)	—
Li_2O ..	n.d.	—	n.d.	tr.	n.d.	tr. ·
Loss on igni-tion ..	—	—	—	35·69†	—	—
TOTAL	100·41	99·92	99·98	100·14	99·98	100·58
Sp. gr. ..	2·75	2·85	2·80	—	2·89	—

* Total Fe calculated as Fe_2O_3.
† $H_2O > 105°C$ including H_2O from any organic H: 10·53. $H_2O < 105°C$: 24·65. CO_2: 0·22.
C: 0·60.

700. Basalt, tholeiitic. Tertiary pillow lava. Creag Mhòr, cliff W. of Beal Point,
Rudha na h-Àirde Glaise, Skye, Inverness-shire. 1-in. 81 Scot., 6-in. 24 S.W.
(1645. Anal., A. D. Wilson and P. Coombs).

S 37872. A microporphyritic grey amygdaloidal rock containing small labradorite phenocrysts in a groundmass of zoned labradorite laths, imperfectly
crystallized purple pyroxene, abundant rounded areas of brownish-green
chloritic material and a black glassy mesostasis. Numerous amygdales contain
brown chloritic material or ankeritic calcite.
S.P. 1954 (1955), p. 60.

701. Olivine-basalt, haematitized. Bole at top of Tertiary lava flow. Creag Mhòr,
cliff W. of Beal Point, Rudha na h-Àirde Glaise, Skye, Inverness-shire. 1-in.
81 Scot., 6-in. 24 S.W. (1579. Anal., W, F. Waters and K. L. H. Murray).
S 37875. An olivine-basalt heavily impregnated with haematite and containing
small quantities of zeolites.
S.P. 1951 (1953), p. 63.

702. Palagonite-tuff. Interbasaltic deposit in Tertiary Volcanic Series. Stream,
1500 yd S. E. of Blackhill, Edinbain, Skye, Inverness-shire. 1-in. 80 Scot., 6-in.
22 N.E. (1086. Anal., G. A. Sergeant).
S 33954-5. A dark-brown resinous palagonite-tuff, composed of fragments of
orthoclase and rare oligoclase and labradorite with biotite and aegirine-augite
in a reddish-brown glass devitrified in streaks to a mass of greenish spherules.

703. Mugearite. Tertiary lava. 50 ft above base of columnar lava, 170 ft thick,
forming cap of Hartaval, S.E. slope of Bealach Hartaval, Trotternish, Skye,
Inverness-shire. 1-in. 80 Scot., 6-in. 17 N.E. (1580. Anal., W. F. Waters and
K. L. H. Murray).
S 37876. A dark-grey mugearite composed of small phenocrysts, often idiomorphic, of fresh olivine and andesine zoned to oligoclase in a base of laths of
oligoclase with plentiful granular augite and coarser opaque ore, a little interstitial chlorite and alkali-feldspar. The rock exhibits a marked flow texture.
S.P. 1951 (1953), p. 63.

704. Andesine-mugearite. Lower Carboniferous lava. Scarp below trigonometrical
height 519, S.W. side of Craigmarloch Wood, 1½ miles N.W. of Kilmacolm,
Renfrewshire. 1-in. 30 Scot., 6-in. 6 N.E. (917. Anal., B. E. Dixon).
S 28077. An andesine-mugearite, composed of a mass of laths of andesine
zoned to albite-oligoclase, abundant granules of augite and magnetite and
pseudomorphs after olivine in opaque iron ore, chlorite and a little quartz.
There is a marked flow texture. Slender needles of apatite are plentiful.
S.P. 1932, Pt II (1933), p. 88; pl. viii, fig. 3.
See also No. **660.**

ALBITE-DIABASES, ETC.

705. Olivine-basalt, albitized and zeolitized. Lower Old Red Sandstone lava. Scarp
80 yd E. of Balvaird Farm, 2½ miles N.E. of Arngask, Perthshire. 1-in. 40 Scot.,
6-in. 120 N.E. (1528. Anal., W. F. Waters; spect. det., J. A. C. McClelland).
S 37268. A grey olivine-basalt. Labradorite phenocrysts, extensively replaced
by albite, are set in a very fine-grained groundmass containing abundant ore
granules. Ferromagnesian minerals are represented by pseudomorphs in
opaque ore. Abundant irregular patches of chlorite and zeolites, mainly
natrolite, in part fill amygdales but probably also represent devitrified mesostasis.
A little carbonate is present.

706. Diabase. Carrock Fell Complex, post-Borrowdale Volcanic Series (Ordovician),
probably Old Red Sandstone. 720 yd N. 57° E. of trigonometrical height 2174,
Carrock Fell, Cumberland. 1-in. 23, 6-in. 48 S.W. (942. Anal., B. E. Dixon).
E 16182. A grey altered quartz-dolerite composed of rather rounded crystals
of pale-coloured pyroxene partly replaced by amphibole and chlorite, tablets
of plagioclase mainly altered to a turbid brown mixture of sericite, chlorite,
possibly kaolin, scattered ore granules and interstitial quartz, alkali-feldspar

and micropegmatite. The ore granules are mainly altered to leucoxene. Sphene and epidote are common accessories. Some pseudomorphs in amphibole and chlorite may represent orthopyroxene.
See also Nos. **615, 629, 650, 675, 688, 743-4.**

707. Olivine-diabase. Sill, Carboniferous or Permo-Carboniferous. 42 ft below top of sill, Stankards No. 2 Borehole, near Uphall, Linlithgowshire. 1-in. 32 Scot., 6-in. 6 S.W. (921. Anal., B. E. Dixon).
S 27975. A mottled grey albitized olivine-dolerite composed of fresh augite ophitically moulded upon feldspar laths commonly 2 mm in length. The feldspars show pronounced zoning from labradorite to albite. Brownish and greenish chloritic alteration products, in part representing original olivine, are present in considerable quantity in compact aggregates. Apatite and opaque ores, including ilmenite partly altered to leucoxene, are accessory.
S.P. 1931, Pt. I (1932), p. 80. *S.P.* 1931, Pt. II (1932), p. 150.
See also Nos. **720, 725.**

	ALBITE-DIABASES, ETC.				
	705	706	707	708	709
SiO_2	57·98	48·51	47·66	42·65	36·89
Al_2O_3	14·39	16·83	14·03	14·58	13·97
Fe_2O_3	7·36	1·85	3·13	1·79	1·42
FeO	1·28	7·39	6·04	10·17	13·47
MgO	4·55	6·78	9·65	7·93	3·98
CaO	3·98	10·84	7·74	6·22	6·02
Na_2O	3·41	2·36	2·93	3·12	2·76
K_2O	1·57	1·25	0·84	0·30	1·31
$H_2O > 105°C$	2·16	2·27	3·06	5·47	2·79
$H_2O < 105°C$	1·66	0·19	2·81	1·38	1·10
TiO_2	1·26	1·20	1·62	1·59	1·70
P_2O_5	0·29	0·18	0·27	0·31	0·32
MnO	0·04	0·15	0·16	0·18	0·26
CO_2	0·42	—	tr.	4·07	14·40
ZrO_2	n.d.(s)	—	—	—	—
SO_3	—	—	—	tr.	—
Cl	—	—	—	tr.	tr.
S	0·01	—	—	0·05	0·04
FeS_2	—	0·05	0·10	—	—
Cr_2O_3	0·01	0·04	0·12	0·04	0·04
V_2O_3	tr.(s)	—	—	tr.(s)	0·01(s)
NiO	tr.(s)	—	—	tr.(s)	tr.(s)
CoO	—	—	—	n.d.(s)	n.d.(s)
BaO	0·04	—	—	tr.(s)	tr.(s)
SrO	tr.(s)	—	—	0·04(s)	0·04(s)
Li_2O	—	—	—	n.d.	n.d.(s)
Pt	—	—	—	n.d.(s)	n.d.(s)
TOTAL	100·41	99·89	100·16	99·89	100·52
Sp. gr.	2·68	—	—	2·73	2·88

708. Albite-diabase. Sill intruded near base of Coal Measures. 2337-47 ft deep, Winkburn Borehole No. G.1, near Caunton, Nottinghamshire. 1-in. 113, 6-in. 30 N.W. (1478. Anal., W. F. Waters; spect. det., J. A. C. McClelland).
E 21665-6. An albitized and chloritized dolerite composed of laths of albite-oligoclase containing abundant threads and films of chlorite, and pseudomorphs in chlorite and in bowlingite after ferromagnesian minerals. Chlorite

is also present in spherulitic and vermicular aggregates filling amygdales. Ilmenite granules, in part altered to leucoxene, are common and calcite forms irregular veins and patches.

709. Albite-diabase. Sill intruded near base of Coal Measures. 2195 ft deep, Kelham Hills Borehole No. 10, Kelham, Nottinghamshire. 1-in. 113, 6-in. 30 S.W. (1479. Anal., W. F. Waters; spect. det., J. A. C. McClelland).
E 21705. A pale greenish-grey very altered dolerite. Feldspar laths are in part replaced by albite-oligoclase and contain abundant chlorite inclusions, and are in part represented by pseudomorphs in ankerite and micaceous minerals. Ferromagnesian minerals, probably including olivine and pyroxene, are represented by pseudomorphs in ankerite. Accessory minerals include ilmenite, leucoxene, pyrite and quartz. Veinlets traversing the rock are composed of carbonate and quartz. Occasional amygdales contain vermicular chlorite.

ALKALI-BASALTS, ETC.

710. Spilite. Lava, Ballantrae Igneous Complex, Ordovician. Cliff at Port Vad, N. of Bennane Head, Ayrshire. 1-in. 7 Scot., 6-in. 60 S.E. (909. Anal., B. E. Dixon).
S 27372. A purplish-brown rock containing phenocrysts of albitized plagioclase, crowded with minute inclusions, in a base of small albite laths, granular iron ore, sphene and epidote cemented by chlorite. Amygdales filled with chlorite or calcite rimmed by chlorite are plentiful.
See also Nos. **618, 686, 696, 728.**

711. Olivine-analcite-dolerite. Sill in Coal Measures. Typical of depth range 2239-2300 ft, Bulcote Borehole, 1450 yd S. of Lowdham Church, 1260 yd W. of Marlock House, 5 miles N.E. of Nottingham, Nottinghamshire. 1-in. 126, 6-in. 39 N.W. (1573. Anal., W. F. Waters and K. L. H. Murray; spect. det., J. A. C. McClelland).
E 23936. A dark-grey analcite-bearing olivine-dolerite containing phenocrysts of augite up to several millimetres across enclosing labradorite laths, and phenocrysts of partly serpentinized olivine. Chlorite in spherulitic intergrowths is interstitial to the feldspar and there is a mesostasis of glass and analcite. Opaque iron ore is plentiful and there are numerous needles of apatite.

712. Olivine-analcite-dolerite. Sill in Coal Measures. 2206 ft deep, Cotgrave Bridge Borehole, 1600 yd N. of Cotgrave Church, 900 yd S.E. of Cotgrave Place, 5 miles S.E. of Nottingham, Nottinghamshire. 1-in. 126, 6-in. 43 S.W. (1574. Anal., W. F. Waters and K. L. H. Murray; spect. det., J. A. C. McClelland).
E 23937. A dark-grey rock composed of phenocrysts of olivine, largely altered to bowlingitic aggregates, and large phenocrysts of slightly purple titanaugite ophitically enclosing laths of labradorite. Chlorite is abundant as inclusions in the feldspar and interstitially. Turbid devitrified glass and analcite are also common interstitially and there are small quantities of fibrous zeolites including thomsonite. Accessory minerals include needles of apatite and opaque iron ore granules.

713. Teschenite. The Brockhill Dyke, post-Downtonian (Old Red Sandstone), probably Carboniferous. Quarry, 250 yd N.W. of Brockhill, Shelsley Beauchamp, Worcestershire. 1-in. 182, 6-in. 20 S.W. (1044. Anal., C. O. Harvey).
E 17757. A fairly coarse grey rock composed of prisms of slightly purple titanaugite and apple-green pseudomorphs in serpentine after olivine set in a base of plagioclase laths, zoned from labradorite to oligoclase, with abundant interstitial analcite and a little natrolite in radial aggregates. Prisms of orthoclase are common and there are abundant hypidiomorphic crystals of magnetite and ilmenite. Chlorite is present both interstitially and replacing plagioclase. Apatite needles are abundant and there is accessory biotite.
S.P. 1938 (1940), p. 95. Min. Mag., vol. xxv, 1940, p. 542.

	SPILITE	ALKALI-DOLERITES		
	710	711	712	713
SiO_2	48·89	47·96	47·36	46·28
Al_2O_3	18·87	14·42	13·72	14·90
Fe_2O_3	2·55	2·49	2·46	3·52
FeO	5·77	8·97	10·09	7·13
MgO	3·84	7·96	9·61	6·12
CaO	7·56	7·97	6·99	6·58
Na_2O	4·14	3·86	3·39	4·49
K_2O	1·06	0·78	0·65	1·72
$H_2O > 105°C$	2·93	2·33	3·43	4·36
$H_2O < 105°C$	0·66	1·18	0·76	1·28
TiO_2	2·42	1·77	1·53	2·56
P_2O_5	0·39	0·26	0·25	0·74
MnO	—	0·16	0·18	0·54
CO_2	0·80	0·08	0·01	tr.
SO_3	—	—	—	0·01
Cl	—	—	—	tr.
F	—	—	—	0·04
S	—	0·03	0·03	—
FeS_2	0·10	—.	—	0·20
V_2O_3	—	tr.(s)	tr.(s)	—
Cr_2O_3	—	0·04	0·05	tr.
NiO	—	tr.(s)	tr.(s)	—
BaO	—	0·01	0·01	0·05
SrO	—	0·01(s)	0·01(s)	—
Li_2O	n.d.	tr.	tr.	—
TOTAL	99·98	100·28	100·53	100·52
Less O for S, F	—	0·01	0·01	0·02
	99·98	100·27	100·52	100·50
Sp. gr.	—	—	—	2·71

714. Monchiquite. Dyke cutting Old Red Sandstone. Ward Holm, Copinsay, Orkney. 1-in. 118 Scot., 6-in. 116 S.W. (957. Anal., B. E. Dixon).
S 29636. A markedly porphryitic dark-grey monchiquite in which the porphyritic constituents are augite, often having a greenish core and a purple rim, and corroded brown hornblende. Pseudomorphs in chlorite and carbonate represent original olivine. The groundmass is composed of abundant small augite prisms and abundant grains of opaque iron ore with a mesostasis of glass or analcite partly replaced by a deep-brown microcrystalline aggregate of carbonate, zeolites and serpentinous minerals. Biotite flakes and apatite needles are common. Amygdales contain serpentinous minerals and analcite.
S.P. 1933, Pt. I (1934), p. 90. *M.G.S.* ' Orkneys ', 1935, p. 182.

715. Nepheline-monchiquite. Dyke cutting Old Red Sandstone. Crockness, Walls, Hoy, Orkney. 1-in. 117 Scot., 6-in. 119 S.W. (912. Anal., B. E. Dixon).
S 27539. A dark-grey rock containing idiomorphic phenocrysts of olivine, partly altered to serpentine, in a groundmass of pyroxene prisms, iron ore granules, small nepheline prisms and a mesostasis of analcite containing apatite needles.
S.P. 1931, Pt. I (1932), p. 79. *M.G.S.* ' Orkneys ', 1935, p. 182.

716. Biotite-monchiquite. Dyke cutting Old Red Sandstone. Rennibister Point, ¼ mile N. of Rennibister Farm, Firth, Orkney. 1-in. 119 Scot., 6-in. 102 S.W. (956. Anal., B. E. Dixon).

S 29635. A dark-grey rock with numerous amygdales. Scarce idiomorphic phenocrysts of augite and pseudomorphs in bowlingite and carbonate after olivine lie in a base of slender augite prisms, iron ore granules and apatite needles with interstitial granular carbonate, chloritic and serpentinous minerals and zeolites. Idiomorphic sphene is accessory. Coarse ragged plates of pale-brown biotite are abundant, enclosing olivine, augite, iron ore and apatite. Calcite and analcite fill the amygdales.
S.P. 1933, Pt. I (1934), p. 90. *M.G.S.* ' Orkneys ', 1935, p. 182.

	MONCHIQUITES				THERALITE
	714	715	716	717	718
SiO_2 ..	39·22	38·64	36·61	34·93	44·56
Al_2O_3 ..	9·71	10·26	10·27	10·08	11·75
Fe_2O_3 ..	7·66	3·24	3·84	4·57	1·77
FeO	6·83	7·21	5·81	6·05	8·68
MgO ..	10·11	14·51	12·04	12·20	13·31
CaO ..	12·80	13·83	14·14	14·12	10·99
Na_2O ..	1·37	2·73	1·84	2·00	2·46
K_2O ..	1·66	0·75	2·00	1·25	1·56
$H_2O > 105°C$	2·11	3·03	3·81	3·48	1·64
$H_2O < 105°C$	0·89	0·54	0·79	1·13	0·15
TiO_2 ..	4·24	2·83	3·74	2·80	2·27
P_2O_5 ..	1·24	1·47	1·41	1·93	0·31
MnO ..	0·16	0·19	0·16	0·24	0·17
CO_2	1·98	0·53	3·14	4·93	0·03
Cl	—	—	—	—	tr.
S	—	—	—	—	0·02
FeS_2 ..	0·20	0·20	0·33	0·51	—
Fe_7S_8 ..	—	—	—	—	tr.
Cr_2O_3 ..	0·09	0·24	0·07	0·06	0·09
BaO ..	0·04	—	0·14	0·10	0·07
SrO	—	—	tr.	—	—
Li_2O ..	tr.	—	tr.	tr.	tr.
TOTAL	100·31	100·20	100·14	100·38	99·83
Sp. gr. ..	—	—	—	—	3·04

717. Biotite-monchiquite. Dyke cutting Old Red Sandstone. In burn, Naversdale, Orphir, Orkney. 1-in. 119 Scot., 6-in. 107. (958. Anal., B. E. Dixon).
S 29648. Porphyritic constituents in this grey amygdaloidal rock consist of numerous pseudomorphs in bowlingite, magnetite and carbonate after olivine and irregular coarse crystals of biotite enclosing augite, magnetite, apatite and pseudomorphs after olivine. The groundmass is composed of abundant pyroxene prisms, iron ore crystals and interstitial analcite. Numerous small amygdales are filled with analcite and calcite.
S.P. 1933, Pt. I (1934), p. 90. *M.G.S.* ' Orkneys ', 1935, p. 182.

718. Olivine-theralite. The Lugar Sill, Carboniferous or Permian. 612 ft deep, No. 16 Borehole, Lands of Mortonmuir, 1 mile 725 yd E. 12° S. of Darnconner Church and 750 yd W. 18° N. of Mortonmuir Farm, Cronberry, Lugar, Ayrshire. 1-in. 14 Scot., 6-in. 30 S.W. (1446. Anal., G. A. Sergeant).
S 35333. A dark-grey olivine-theralite composed of phenocrysts of fresh olivine in a base of abundant augite granules, plentiful small laths of labradorite and large tablets of biotite moulded upon augite and feldspar. Analcite and nepheline are interstitial. Accessory minerals include a little opaque ore, apatite and occasional prisms of barkevikite.
Trans. Geol. Soc. Glasgow, vol. xxi, 1948, p. 172.
See also Nos. **638, 719.**

PICRITES, PERIDOTITES, SERPENTINES, ETC.

719. Picroteschenite. The Lugar Sill, Carboniferous or Permian. 699 ft deep, No. 16 Borehole, Lands of Mortonmuir, 1 mile 725 yd E. 12° S. of Darnconner Church and 750 yd W. 18° N. of Mortonmuir Farm, Cronberry, Lugar, Ayrshire. 1-in. 14 Scot., 6-in. 30 S.W. (1448. Anal., G. A. Sergeant).
S 36068. A grey augite-rich picroteschenite composed of abundant idiomorphic prisms of augite and bowlingitic pseudomorphs after olivine in a base of coarse-grained labradorite with interstitial analcite and nepheline. Accessory minerals include rare coarse plates of interstitial carbonate, needles of apatite, opaque ore partly altered to leucoxene and tablets of biotite.
Trans. Geol. Soc. Glasgow, vol. xxi, 1948, p. 180.
See also Nos. **638, 718.**

720. Picroteschenite. Sill, Carboniferous or Permo-Carboniferous. 207 ft below top of sill, Stankards No. 2 Borehole, near Uphall, Linlithgowshire. 1-in. 32 Scot., 6-in. 6 S.W. (916. Anal., B. E. Dixon).
S 28003. The rock is composed of abundant pseudomorphs after olivine in yellow-green bowlingite, prisms of fresh purple augite, labradorite zoned to oligoclase, biotite, and abundant interstitial analcite. Apatite needles and granules of opaque ores are accessory.
S.P. 1931, Pt. I (1932), p. 80. *S.P.* 1931, Pt. II (1932), p. 150; pl. iii, fig. 4.
See also Nos. **707, 725.**

	PICROTESCHENITES		PICRITE, PERIDOTITE, SERPENTINES			
	719	720	721	722	723	724
SiO$_2$	47·22	43·82	43·65	42·67	41·92	40·97
Al$_2$O$_3$	13·46	10·60	3·83	0·80	0·37	9·77
Fe$_2$O$_3$	1·68	4·36	2·24	1·98	4·38	4·63
FeO	5·84	6·88	8·61	4·23	1·97	7·25
MgO	8·01	12·77	33·10	37·86	39·31	15·58
CaO	11·38	6·75	3·44	0·25	0·09	6·01
Na$_2$O	3·27	3·14	0·64	0·03	} tr.	2·15
K$_2$O	2·19	1·52	0·19	n.d.		0·78
H$_2$O>105°C	3·55	4·59	2·26	11·46	11·39	5·16
H$_2$O<105°C	0·78	2·66	0·25	0·14	0·15	5·47
TiO$_2$	1·58	2·34	0·23	tr.	—	1·60
P$_2$O$_5$	0·27	0·48	0·06	0·02	tr.	0·29
MnO	0·13	0·17	0·17	0·04	0·09	0·19
CO$_2$	0·40	tr.	0·24	0·10	0·03	0·17
ZrO$_2$	—	—	tr.	—	—	—
SO$_3$	—	—	0·02	—	—	tr.
Cl	tr.	—	tr.	—	—	tr.
S	0·02	—	—	0·02	—	0·05
FeS$_2$	—	0·22	0·03	—	0·07	—.
Fe$_7$S$_8$	—	—	tr.	—	—	—
Cr$_2$O$_3$	0·09	0·11	1·11	0·37	0·30	0·11
V$_2$O$_3$	—	—	—	—	n.d.	n.d.(s)
NiO	—	—	0·24	0·21	} 0·08	tr.(s)
CoO	—	—	—	—		tr.(s)
BaO	0·06	—	tr.	0·01	—	tr.(s)
SrO	—	—	—	—	—	0·03(s)
Li$_2$O	tr.	—	—	n.d.	—	n.d.
Pt	—	—	—	—	—	n.d.(s)
TOTAL	99·93	100·41	100·31	100·19	100·15	100·21
Sp. gr.	2·82	—	3·16	—	2·67	—

721. Peridotite. Intrusion in Lewisian Gneiss. N.W. of burial ground, Maaruig, 8 miles N.E. of Tarbert, Harris, Inverness-shire. 1-in. 99 Scot., 6-in. Hebrides 11 N.W. (1467. Anal., G. A. Sergeant).
S 35784, 36342-7. A dark greenish-grey rock composed of granular olivine showing little serpentinization but traversed by numerous cracks depicted in iron ore, large plates of clinoenstatite and enstatite enclosing olivine, robust prisms of hornblende and scarce phlogopite. There are numerous granules of chromite.
Rep. Mineral Resources Panel, Scottish Council (Development and Industry), ' Serpentine and Olivine-rock in Scotland ', 1954, p. 17. Edinburgh.

722. Antigorite-serpentine. In Unst ' Main Serpentine ', Shetland Metamorphic Series. 650 yd N.E. of S. end of Loch of Cliff, Unst, Shetland. 1-in. 131 Scot., 6-in. 5 N.E. (1583. Anal., W. F. Waters and K. L. H. Murray).
S 38107. A pale greenish-grey antigorite-serpentine composed of closely inter-locked fibres and sheaves of antigorite up to 0·5 mm long enclosing fine granules of magnetite and occasional larger grains with serrated edges of magnetite intergrown with chromite.
S.P. 1951 (1953), p. 63. *Rep. Mineral Resources Panel, Scottish Council (Development and Industry)*, ' Serpentine and Olivine-rock in Scotland ', 1954, p. 16. Edinburgh.

723. Antigorite-serpentine. Intrusion in Fetlar Central Phyllite Group, Shetland Metamorphic Series. 200 yd E. of Mill Burn, about 300 yd from coast, Fetlar, Shetland. 1-in. 130 Scot., 6-in. 12 S.E. (1005. Anal., C. O. Harvey).
S 31643. A greenish-grey rock composed of blades and occasional larger plates of antigorite, scattered small crystals of iron ore and coarser chromite.
S.P. 1936, Pt. I (1937), p. 86. *Geol. Surv. Wartime Pamphlet* No. 9, ' Talc ', 1941, p. 17; 2nd edit. reissue, 1946, p. 17.

724. Picrite. Intrusion in Carboniferous rocks. 3890-3909 ft deep, Long Clawson No. 1 Borehole, Leicestershire. 1-in. 142, 6-in. 13 N.W. (1480. Anal., C. O. Harvey; spect. det., J. A. C. McClelland).
E 20909-10. A mottled dark greenish-grey picrite composed of abundant greenish-brown serpentine, robust prisms of titanaugite and iron ore, subord-inate apatite labradorite, and tablets of deeply coloured biotite, and interstitial analcite.

725. Picrite. Sill, Carboniferous or Permo-Carboniferous. 90 ft below top of sill, Stankards No. 2 Borehole, near Uphall, Linlithgowshire. 1-in. 32 Scot., 6-in. 6 S.W. (915. Anal., B. E. Dixon).
S 27983. A mottled greenish rock containing small hypidiomorphic crystals of olivine partly altered to yellow and green serpentine, and pale reddish-brown fresh augite plates several millimetres across enclosing olivine. There is a little interstitial labradorite, and iron ores are present often in association with dark-brown biotite.
S.P. 1931, Pt. I (1932), p. 80. *S.P.* 1931, Pt. II (1932), p. 151; pl. iii, fig. 1.
See also Nos. **707, 720.**

726. Antigorite-serpentine. Intrusion in schists of Dalradian Series. Crag, 300 yd S. 16° W. of sheepfold on path W. from Corrycharmaig, Glen Lochay, Perth-shire. 1-in. 46 Scot., 6-in. 67 S.E. (1492. Anal., W. F. Waters; spect. det., J. A. C. McClelland).
S 36768. A greenish antigorite-serpentine composed of a felt of antigorite blades with scattered crystals of chromian magnetite.
Geol. Surv. Wartime Pamphlet No. 9, ' Talc ', Supplement No. 1, 1949, p. 4.
See also Nos. **733-4, 818-9, 840.**

727. Enstatite-harrisite. ? Old Red Sandstone. N.E. shore of Moora Waters, North-maven, Shetland. 1-in. 128 Scot., 6-in. 24 S.E. (1065. Anal., C. O. Harvey; spect. det., H. K. Whalley).
S 33683. A dark-grey rock composed of mainly small idiomorphic to rounded olivine crystals partly altered to serpentine and opaque ore, and scarcer plates

of enstatite, pale-brown amphibole and biotite, cemented by a coarse aggregate of labradorite prisms. The olivine crystals are poikilitically enclosed by the other ferromagnesian minerals.

	PICRITE, PERIDOTITE, SERPENTINES				
	725	726	727	728	729
SiO_2 ..	40·84	40·61	40·58	38·58	38·50
Al_2O_3 ..	6·58	2·30	7·57	1·65	0·91
Fe_2O_3 ..	2·59	3·67	3·18	3·94	3·20
FeO	11·61	3·23	9·01	2·49	4·27
MgO ..	23·72	37·52	27·50	37·84	37·82
CaO ..	4·46	0·15	4·51	0·04	1·19
Na_2O ..	0·91	0·02	0·76	0·62	0·31
K_2O ..	0·32	tr.	0·15	0·11	tr.
$H_2O > 105°C$	6·15	11·61	5·74	12·68	12·02
$H_2O < 105°C$	1·22	0·10	0·33	1·49	0·84
TiO_2 · ..	1·29	0·03	0·39	0·04	0·69
P_2O_5 ..	0·21	tr.	0·04	0·04	tr.
MnO ..	0·21	0·08	0·20	—	0·16
CO_2	tr.	n.d.	0·09	0·10	tr.
SO_3	—	n.d.	—	—	—
Cl	—	n.d.	—	—	—
S	—	n.d.	—	—	—
FeS_2 ..	0·06	—	0·11	0·10	tr.
Fe_7S_8 ..	—	—	tr.	—	—
Cr_2O_3 ..	0·10	1·07	0·26	0·24	0·25
V_2O_3 ..	—	tr.(s)	—	—	—
NiO	—	0·15	—	0·06	} 0·21
CoO ..	—	n.d.(s)	—	—	
BaO ..	—	n.d.(s)	0·02	—	—
SrO	—	n.d.(s)	0·01(s)	—	—
Li_2O ..	—	n.d.(s)	—	n.d.	—
Pt	—	n.d.(s)	—	—	—
TOTAL	100·27	100·54	100·45	100·02	100·37
Sp. gr. ..	—	2·67	—	—	—

728. Bastite-serpentine. Ballantrae Igneous Complex, Ordovician. 100 yd S.W. of Balhamie, ¾ mile W. by N. of Colmonell, Ayrshire. 1-in. 7 Scot., 6-in. 66 N.W. (907. Anal., B. E. Dixon).
S 27369. A black rock with abundant bronze-coloured phenocrysts of bastite in a mesh of scales and fibres of serpentine with much secondary ore including a little chromite rimmed by magnetite.
Geol. Mag., vol. lxix, 1932, p. 113.
See also Nos. 618, 686, 696, 710.

729. Bronzite-serpentine. Intrusion in Fetlar Central Phyllite Group, Shetland Metamorphic Series. 200 yd S. of trigonometrical height 406, Busta Hill, Fetlar, Shetland. 1-in. 130 Scot., 6-in. 12 S.E. (926. Anal., B. E. Dixon).
S 28617. A dark greenish-grey rock in which abundant coarse olivine crystals are largely replaced by a very pale serpentine. Bronzite crystals are often rimmed by bowlingite and accessory iron ore is often surrounded by chlorite. Rare brown chromite is present.
S.P. 1932, Pt. I (1933), p. 95. *Geol. Surv. Wartime Pamphlet* No. 9, 'Talc', 1941, p. 17; 2nd edit. reissue, 1946, p. 17.

730. Peridotite-serpentine. Unst ' Main Serpentine ', Shetland Metamorphic Series. 650 yd N.E. of Hagdale, and N. of Wick of Hagdale, Unst, Shetland. 1-in. 131 Scot., 6-in. 5 N.E. (1582. Anal., W. F. Waters and K. L. H. Murray).
S 38106. A dark-grey peridotite-serpentine composed of coarse granular colourless olivine largely altered to antigorite, and plates of pale orthopyroxene often rimmed by bowlingite. Chromite is accessory.
S.P. 1951 (1953), p. 63. *Rep. Mineral Resources Panel, Scottish Council (Development and Industry)*, ' Serpentine and Olivine-rock in Scotland ', 1954, p. 16. Edinburgh.

731. Peridotite. Intrusion in Lewisian Gneiss. 600 yd N.E. of summit of Grose-Clett, Harris, Inverness-shire. 1-in. 99 Scot., 6-in. Hebrides 18 N.E. (1367. Anal., C. O. Harvey; spect. det., J. A. C. McClelland).
S 35689, 35695-8. A lustre-mottled dark-grey rock composed of granular olivine partly converted to serpentine, equidimensional flakes of talc, robust tremolite prisms enclosing olivine, abundant opaque ore, often interstitial, and a little carbonate.
Rep. Mineral Resources Panel, Scottish Council (Development and Industry), ' Serpentine and Olivine-rock in Scotland ', 1954, p. 17. Edinburgh.

732. Dunite-serpentine. Unst ' Main Serpentine ', Shetland Metamorphic Series. 450 yd S.W. of Hagdale and 100 yd S.W. of Hagdale chromite quarry, Unst, Shetland. 1-in. 131 Scot., 6-in. 5 N.E. (1581. Anal., W. F. Waters and K. L. H. Murray).

| | PERIDOTITES, SERPENTINES | | | | |
	730	731	732	733	734
SiO_2	38·00	37·65	33·22	32·8	29·6
Al_2O_3	0·64	1·76	0·72	—	—
Fe_2O_3	3·85	4·99	4·64	6·8†	7·1†
FeO	3·39	6·00	3·44	—	—
MgO	39·58	39·76	40·85	35·5	32·7
CaO	0·93	0·31	0·27	tr.	3·7
Na_2O	0·08	tr.	0·09	—	—
K_2O	n.d.	0·53	0·02	—	—
$H_2O > 105°C$	12·25	6·69	13·97	—	—
$H_2O < 105°C$	0·64	0·26	0·96	tr.	tr.
TiO_2	n.d.	0·09	0·07	—	—
P_2O_5	0·02	0·04	0·01	—	—
MnO	0·11	0·20	0·11	—	—
CO_2	0·15	0·30	0·57	—	—
S	0·04	0·01	0·01	—	—
Cr_2O_3	0·39	1·50	1·23	0·4	1·2
NiO	0·23	—*	0·19	—	—
BaO	0·01	—	tr.	—	—
Li_2O	n.d.	—	n.d.	—	—
Loss on ignition	—	—	—	23·7	25·5
TOTAL	100·31	100·09	100·37	—‡	—§
Sp. gr.	—	—	2·63	—	—

* NiO(s) about 0·3%.
† Total Fe calculated as Fe_2O_3.
‡ Acid-soluble portion:—Fe as Fe_2O_3: 3·0%. CaO: tr. MgO: 17·5%.
§ Acid-soluble portion:—Fe as Fe_2O_3: 4·1%. CaO: 3·3%. MgO: 17·4%.

S 38105. A dark greenish-grey rock composed of antigorite enclosing relict olivine and rounded crystals of chromite rimmed by magnetite. A little ore is enclosed in veinlets of chlorite and carbonate.
S.P. 1951 (1953), p. 63. *Rep. Mineral Resources Panel, Scottish Council* (*Development and Industry*), ' Serpentine and Olivine-rock in Scotland ', 1954, p. 16. Edinburgh.

733. **Carbonated talcose serpentine.** Intrusive mass in schists of Dalradian Series. 135 yd N.W. of old chromite workings, ½ mile S. of W. of Corrycharmaig, Glen Lochay, Perthshire. 1-in. 46 Scot., 6-in. 67 S.E. (1124. Anal., C. O. Harvey).
S 34396. A yellowish-grey mottled rock composed of coarsely granular breunnerite enclosing discrete flakes of talc and set with granular iron ore in a matrix of talc.
Geol. Surv. Wartime Pamphlet No. 9, ' Talc ', 1941, p. 17; 2nd edit. reissue, 1946, p. 17; Supplement No. 1, 1949, p. 6.
See also Nos. **726, 734, 818-9, 840.**

734. **Carbonated talcose serpentine.** Intrusive mass in schists of Dalradian Series. Old chromite workings, ½ mile S. of W. of Corrycharmaig, Glen Lochay, Perthshire. 1-in. 46 Scot., 6-in. 67 S.E. (1125. Anal., C. O. Harvey).
S 34397-8. A sheared mottled yellowish-grey and grey rock composed of granular carbonate, including dolomite and breunnerite, in a matrix of talc. There are numerous crystals of chromian magnetite and a little pyrite.
Geol. Surv. Wartime Pamphlet No. 9, ' Talc ', 1941, p. 17; 2nd edit. reissue, 1946, p. 17; Supplement No. 1, 1949, p. 6.
See also Nos. **726, 733, 818-9, 840.**

II. PARTIAL ANALYSES OF IGNEOUS ROCKS

735. Grorudite. Sill, post-Cambrian. 230 yd S. by E. of S. end of Lochan Bealach na Uidhe, Assynt, Sutherland. 1-in. 107 Scot., 6-in. 71 N.E. (1552. Anal., E. C. W. Maycock; spect. det., J. A. C. McClelland). S 38717.
Mg: 0·085%. Li: tr., <0·005%(s). Ni: n.d., <0·01%(s).

736. Quartz-syenite. Part of major intrusion, post-Cambrian. Allt a' Bhrisdidh, flat part of hillside, Cnoc na Sròine, Assynt, Sutherland. 1-in. 101 Scot., 6-in. 91 N.W. (1551. Anal., E. C. W. Maycock; spect. det., J. A. C. McClelland). S 38810.
Mg: 0·025%. Li: tr., <0·005%(s). Ni: n.d., <0·01%(s).
See also Nos. 738-40, 746.

737. Felsite. Dyke in Lewisian, post-Cambrian. Fairait Mhòr, Achmelvich, near Lochinver, Sutherland. 1-in. 107 Scot., 6-in. 69 N.W. (1591. Anal., K. L. H. Murray). S 38132.
Min. Mag., vol. xxix, 1952, p. 829.
Cl: 0·01%.

738. Syenite. Part of major intrusion, post-Cambrian. N. slopes of Cnoc na Sròine, 1050 yd S.E. of Loyne Road Bridge, Assynt, Sutherland. 1-in. 101 Scot., 6-in. 82 S.E. (1232-4. Anal., C. O. Harvey). Fractions of syenite separated magnetically by A. F. Hallimond.
Geol. Surv. Wartime Pamphlet No. 44, ' Scottish Sources of Alkali Feldspar ', 1945, p. 22.
1232 (Rock).—Total Fe calculated as Fe_2O_3: 3·2%.
1233 (1st tailing).—Total Fe calculated as Fe_2O_3: 0·9%. Na_2O: 5·9%. K_2O: 7·5%.
1234 (2nd tailing).—Total Fe calculated as Fe_2O_3: 0·5%.
See also Nos. 736, 739-40, 746.

739. Syenite. Part of major intrusion, post-Cambrian. W. slopes of Cnoc na Sròine, 1700 yd N.W. of Altnacealgach Hotel and 250 yd N.E. of road, Assynt, Sutherland. 1-in. 101 Scot., 6-in. 91 N.E. (1235-7. Anal., C. O. Harvey).
Fractions of syenite separated magnetically by A. F. Hallimond.
Geol. Surv. Wartime Pamphlet No. 44, ' Scottish Sources of Alkali Feldspar ', 1945, p. 22.
1235 (Rock).—Total Fe calculated as Fe_2O_3: 3·3%.
1236 (1st tailing).—Total Fe calculated as Fe_2O_3: 0·4%. Na_2O: 6·5%. K_2O: 3·6%.
1237 (2nd tailing).—Total Fe calculated as Fe_2O_3: 0·3%.
See also Nos. 736, 738, 740, 746.

740. Ledmorite. Part of major intrusion, post-Cambrian. Cnoc na Sròine, 200 yd S.E. of Ledmore, Assynt, Sutherland. 1-in. 101 Scot., 6-in. 91 N.W. (1554. Anal., E. C. W. Maycock; spect. det., J. A. C. McClelland). S 38801.
Mg: 3·0%. Li: tr., <0·005%(s). Ni: n.d., <0·01%(s).
See also Nos. 736, 738-9, 746.

741. Hornblende-porphyrite. Sill, post-Cambrian. 380 yd. E. 25° S. of outflow of large loch on Allt a' Chalda Mòr, Assynt, Sutherland. 1-in. 107 Scot., 6-in. 71 N.E. (1555. Anal., E. C. W. Maycock; spect. det., J. A. C. McClelland). S 37317.
Mg: 4·0%. Li: tr., <0·005%(s). Ni: n.d., <0·01%(s).

742. Vogesite. Sill, post-Cambrian. 530 yd W. 25° S. of junction in wall, 150 yd N. of Cnoc Gorm, Assynt, Sutherland. 1-in. 107 Scot., 6-in. 71 N.E. (1556. Anal., E. C. W. Maycock; spect. det., J. A. C. McClelland). S 37305.
Mg: 2·6%. Li: tr., <0·005%(s). Ni: n.d., <0·01%(s).

743. Quartz-gabbro. Carrock Fell Complex, post-Borrowdale Volcanic Series (Ordovician), probably Old Red Sandstone. Normal Carrock Fell Gabbro, 1 ft

from limit of contamination by Eycott lava type xenolith (No. **809**). Crag, 770 yd N. 36° W. of Mosedale Bridge over River Caldew, Mosedale, Cumberland. 1-in. 23, 6-in. 48 S.W. (1560. Anal., K. L. H. Murray). E 23495.
Na_2O: 3·13%. K_2O: 1·38%.
See also Nos. **615, 629, 650, 675, 688, 706, 744.**

744. Quartz-gabbro, contaminated. Carrock Fell Complex, post-Borrowdale Volcanic Series (Ordovician), probably Old Red Sandstone. Transition zone between Eycott lava type xenolith (No. **809**) and Carrock Fell Gabbro (No. **743**). Crag, 770 yd N. 36° W. of Mosedale Bridge over River Caldew, Mosedale, Cumberland. 1-in. 23, 6-in. 48 S.W. (1559. Anal., K. L. H. Murray). E 23494A.
Na_2O: 3·83%. K_2O: 1·41%.
See also Nos. **615, 629, 650, 675, 688, 706, 743.**

745. Dunite. Plutonic intrusion, Tertiary. Stream, immediately above road bridge, $\frac{3}{4}$ mile N. 40° E. of Harris Lodge, Island of Rum, Inverness-shire. 1-in. 60 Scot., 6-in. Skye 66 N.E. (1368. Anal., C. O. Harvey; spect. det., J. A. C. McClelland). S 35685, 35699.
Rep. Mineral Resources Panel, Scottish Council (*Development and Industry*), ' Serpentine and Olivine-rock in Scotland ', 1954, p. 17. Edinburgh.
SiO_2: 40·13%. Al_2O_3: 1·14%. Total Fe calculated as Fe_2O_3: 10·12%. $H_2O < 105°C$: 0·05%. TiO_2: 0·09%. P_2O_5: 0·04%. MnO: 0·20%. Cr_2O_3: 0·74%. NiO: probably 0·3%(s).

746. Cromaltite. Part of major intrusion, post-Cambrian. Bad na h'Achlaise, 680 yd from Ledmore River, S. of Ledmore, Assynt, Sutherland. 1-in. 101 Scot., 6-in. 91 N.W. (1553. Anal., E. C. W. Maycock; spect. det., J. A. C. McClelland). S 38774.
Mg: 3·8%. Li: tr.,<0·005%. Ni: n.d.,<0·01%.
See also Nos. **736, 738-40.**

III. ANALYSES OF METAMORPHIC ROCKS

ORTHOGNEISSES

	ORTHOGNEISSES			
	747	748	749	750
SiO_2	65·47	61·99	59·92	48·08
Al_2O_3	14·87	17·41	17·44	11·95
Fe_2O_3	1·11	1·85	2·24	4·39
FeO	3·43	2·44	3·35	12·28
MgO	2·61	2·32	2·41	5·51
CaO	4·29	4·79	7·58	9·35
Na_2O	3·81	5·68	4·76	2·10
K_2O	2·22	1·82	0·40	0·43
$H_2O > 105°C$	0·88	0·63	0·78	1·57
$H_2O < 105°C$	0·04	0·08	0·05	0·16
TiO_2	0·48	0·84	0·76	3·59
P_2O_5	0·12	0·36	0·23	0·32
MnO	0·07	0·06	0·09	0·26
CO_2	0·39	tr.	tr.	tr.
Cl	tr.	—	tr.	tr.
F	tr.	—	—	—
S	0·01	—	n.d.	0·01
Cr_2O_3	0·02	—	n.d.	0·01
V_2O_3	—	—	—	0·08
BaO	0·07	—	tr.	tr.
SrO	0·03(s)	—	0·08(s)	0·03(s)
Rb_2O	0·01(s)	—	—	—
TOTAL	99·93	100·27	100·09	100·12
Sp. gr.	2·77	—	2·82	3·14

747. Biotite-epidote-albite-gneiss. Hornblendic Group in core of Morar anticline ('Sub-Moine'). Shore, 660 yd E. 10° N. of Glaschoille House, Knoydart, Inverness-shire. 1-in. 61 Scot., 6-in. 91 S.E. (1059. Anal., C. O. Harvey; spect. det., H. K. Whalley).
S 33430. A finely striped grey rock in which biotite tablets and prisms of epidote and zoisite occur in bands in a granular base of quartz, albite and orthoclase. There are plentiful small idiomorphic sphene crystals and iron ore is accessory.

748. Albite-orthogneiss. Shetland Metamorphic Series. Grut Ness, 1¼ miles E. of Uyea, North Roe, Shetland. 1-in. 130 Scot., 6-in. 9 S.E. (961. Anal., B. E. Dixon).
S 29706. A rudely banded pink and grey rock composed of coarse tablets of albite with aggregates of green biotite and aggregates of epidote in a finely granular mosaic of quartz. The albite is crowded with idiomorphic flakes of white mica and prisms of epidote and zoisite. Pyrite, rutile and sphene are accessory.
S.P. 1933, Pt. I (1934), p. 90.

749. Hornblende-gneiss. In core of Morar anticline ('Sub-Moine'). E. bank of tributary of Beasdale Burn, 1000 yd S. 35° W. of trigonometrical height 1972 (summit), Sìthean Mòr, South Morar, Inverness-shire. 1-in. 61 Scot., 6-in. 121 S.E. (1058. Anal., C. O. Harvey; spect. det., H. K. Whalley).
S 32735. A grey and white striped and banded acid hornblende-gneiss composed of rather elongate prisms of bluish hornblende in a granular groundmass of quartz and oligoclase. Iron ore, epidote and apatite are accessory. Much of the feldspar is clouded with alteration products.

750. Garnetiferous hornblende-gneiss. In core of Morar anticline (' Sub-Moine '). 660 yd. S.W. of trigonometrical height 1972 (summit), Sithean Mòr, South Morar, Inverness-shire. 1-in. 61 Scot., 6-in. 121 S.E. (1057. Anal., C. O. Harvey; spect. det., H. K. Whalley).
S 32734. A dark-grey striped gneiss with small pink garnets. Microscopically the rock is composed of well-foliated aggregates of small hornblende prisms, rounded sphene crystals and plentiful iron ore, irregularly interbanded with granular quartz and oligoclase. Scattered allotriomorphic garnets contain inclusions of quartz and iron ore. Epidote and apatite are accessory.

EPIDIORITES, HORNBLENDE-SCHIST, GREEN SCHISTS, ETC.

751. Lamproschist. Minor intrusion in Moine permeation granite-gneiss. Allt an Fhaing, 1100 yd S. 34° W. of Callop, near Loch Shiel, Argyllshire. 1-in. 62 Scot., 6-in. 5 S.W. (1652. Anal., A. D. Wilson and P. Coombs; spect. det., C. O. Harvey and K. L. H. Murray).
S 40424. A grey schistose rock containing abundant uniformly-orientated tablets of greenish-brown biotite and prisms of hornblende in a mosaic of quartz and andesine. The hornblende is often in coarse irregular prisms of bluish colour and rich in minute ore inclusions. Small crystals of epidote are common and idiomorphic sphene and prismatic apatite are present in small quantity.
S.P. 1954 (1955), p. 60.

752. Epidiorite. Dyke in gabbro, Lizard Complex, pre-Devonian. Quarry on S. side of Porthoustock Cove, St. Keverne, Cornwall. 1-in. 359, 6-in. 81 N.E. (939. Anal., B. E. Dixon).
E 15960-1. A dark greenish-grey epidiorite or metadolerite in which the original igneous texture is apparent. The rock is composed of albite, ragged crystals of pale-green amphibole and abundant skeletal leucoxene crystals. Accessory minerals include sphene and zircon. Lines of movement traverse the rock and there are veinlets composed of calcite, prehnite and a little quartz.
S.P. 1932, Pt. I (1933), p. 96.
See also No. **764.**

753. Foliated basic rock. Sheet, intrusion in phyllites, Shetland Metamorphic Series. Field immediately behind Mouswall farmhouse, Tingwall, Shetland. 1-in. 128 Scot., 6-in. 52 N.E. (930. Anal., B. E. Dixon).
S 28392. A grey rock composed of coarse ragged plates of hornblende fringed by bluish, more sodic amphibole blades, spongy ore crystals and coarse irregular andesine tablets poikiloblastically enclosing abundant hornblende prisms. Much of the feldspar possesses a granulitized texture.
S.P. 1932, Pt. I (1933), p. 96.

754. Hornblende-feldspar-rock. Intrusion in kyanite-bearing gneiss, Shetland Metamorphic Series. Road at North Voe, 550 yd due E. of Salt Ness, Symbister, Whalsey, Shetland. 1-in. 128 Scot., 6-in. 38 N.E. (968. Anal., B. E. Dixon).
S 30033. A mottled green and lilac rock composed of coarse plates of labradorite containing patches of sericite, ragged hornblende prisms sometimes containing abundant minute inclusions of iron ore, and aggregates of bluish-green amphibole blades. There are robust idiomorphic prisms of epidote, and pyrite, apatite and secondary chlorite are also present. Prehnite occurs in sheaves of scales.
S.P. 1934, Pt. I (1935), p. 83.

755. Garnetiferous hornblende-schist. In semipelitic injected Moine Schist. East side of road, 335 yd S. 35° E of Salen Inn, Loch Sunart, Argyllshire. 1-in. 52 Scot., 6-in. 26 N.E. (1545. Anal., W. F. Waters and K. L. H. Murray).
S 37580. A black lustrous rock with prominent pink garnets, composed of a hypidiomorphic aggregate of hornblende prisms with coarse-grained quartz,

	EPIDIORITES, ETC.				HORNBLENDE-·SCHIST
	751	752	753	754	755
SiO_2	59·26	50·90	49·81	49·06	46·91
Al_2O_3	17·55	15·06	15·97	24·07	14·31
Fe_2O_3	1·06	0·93	1·13	0·85	8·69
FeO	4·35	7·13	9·61	5·07	5·99
MgO	3·19	7·31	4·93	5·43	6·81
CaO	4·93	9·98	8·94	8·58	10·15
Na_2O	4·68	3·51	4·12	3·07	1·11
K_2O	2·16	0·68	0·59	0·94	0·77
$H_2O > 105°C$	1·16	1·21	0·92	1·78	1·03
$H_2O < 105°C$	0·12	0·32	0·10	0·18	0·07
TiO_2	0·99	2·50	3·05	0·63	3·44
P_2O_5	0·34	0·23	0·44	0·24	0·42
MnO	0·11	0·18	0·18	0·06	0·28
CO_2	tr.	0·20	0·12	0·16	0·20
S	0·03	—	—	—	0·01
FeS_2	—	—	0·12	0·25	—
Fe_7S_8	—	—	—	tr.	—
Cr_2O_3	tr.	0·05	0·02	tr.	0·03
NiO	—	—	—	—	tr.
BaO	0·13	—	—	—	0·02
Li_2O	—	—	—	tr.	—
Rarer oxides	0·13(s)*	—	—	—	—
TOTAL	100·19	100·19	100·05	100·37	100·24
Sp. gr.	2·78	—	—	—	—

* Present in approximately the following percentages:—ZrO_2: 0·04. Cr_2O_3: 0·001. V_2O_3: 0·01. SrO: 0·07. Ga_2O_3: 0·005. Yt_2O_3: <0·01.

granular opaque ore, sphene and a little feldspar altered to a micaceous aggregate. Allotriomorphic garnets contain inclusions of the other minerals. Apatite and carbonate are accessory.

756. Albite-epidote-amphibolite. Start Green Schists. Limebury Point, Rickham Common, Salcombe Estuary, Devonshire. 1-in. 355, 6-in. 138 N.E. (989. Anal., C. O. Harvey).
E 17024. A pale greyish-green schistose rock composed of a fine-grained aggregate of pale hornblende prisms and shreds, clinozoisite prisms, albite often aggregated into lenticular bands, abundant finely granular sphene and chlorite.
S.P. 1935, Pt. I (1936), p. 93. *Geol. Mag.*, vol. lxxv, 1938, p. 507.

757. Hornblende-epidote-albite-rock. A variety of green schist of the Central Group of Fetlar, Shetland Metamorphic Series. Between Wirr Geo and Mussi Geo, 450 yd N. 32° W. of Everland, Fetlar, Shetland. 1-in. 130 Scot., 6-in. 18 N.W. (925. Anal., B. E. Dixon).
S 28616. A greenish-grey sheared rock composed of porphyroblasts of albite, sometimes granulitized and containing abundant zoisite prisms, lenticular aggregates of hornblende and chlorite, occasional patches of calcite, abundant idiomorphic crystals and granules of sphene and scarce idiomorphic pyrite crystals. The rock is traversed by irregular veinlets of epidote and calcite.
S.P. 1932, Pt. I (1933), p. 95.

758. Amphibole-talc-chlorite-schist. Start Green Schists. Shore at Limebury Point, Rickham Common, Salcombe Estuary, Devonshire. 1-in. 355, 6-in. 138 N.E. (988. Anal., B. E. Dixon).

cf E 17034. A pale greenish-white rock with occasional coarse talc flakes, microscopically composed of contorted folia of pale amphibole prisms with subordinate talc, sometimes forming porphyroblasts, and abundant colourless chlorite in small flakes. A little sphene is accessory.

Zeits. Krist., vol. xciv, 1936, p. 280. *Geol. Mag.*, vol. lxxv, 1938, p. 507.

	GREEN SCHISTS, ETC.			
	756	757	758	759
SiO_2	47·86	46·89	44·77	35·89
Al_2O_3	17·01	17·06	10·24	21·09
Fe_2O_3	2·60*	2·17	0·48	4·69*
FeO	6·05*	6·40	8·82	10·32*
MgO	9·42	7·45	20·54	8·89
CaO	9·56	8·81	7·99	10·32
Na_2O	2·84	3·77	0·25	0·70
K_2O	0·17	0·41	0·37	0·06
$H_2O > 105°C$	2·75	3·12	5·12	5·41
$H_2O < 105°C$	0·25	0·17	0·15	0·24
TiO_2	1·05	2·41	0·93	1·53
P_2O_5	0·05	0·29	tr.	0·10
MnO	0·21	0·11	0·25	0·25
CO_2	tr.	0·75	—	tr.
F	—	—	n.d.	—
FeS_2	—	0·08	tr.	—
Cr_2O_3	0·03	0·10	0·19	0·04
NiO .. .. .. }	—	—	0·12	—
CoO .. .. .. }				
C	0·07	—	—	0·29
TOTAL	99·92	99·99	100·22	99·82

* Figures approximate owing to presence of organic matter.

759. Chlorite-epidote-schist. Start Green Schists. Shore at Limebury Point, Rickham Common, Salcombe Estuary, Devonshire. 1-in. 355, 6-in. 138 N.E. (990. Anal., C. O. Harvey).

E 17032. A green schistose rock composed of aggregates of granular epidote cemented by chlorite (prochlorite), a little fibrous amphibole, lenticles and pods of albite with a little quartz, films of carbonaceous material and granular sphene.

S.P. 1935, Pt. I (1936), p. 93. *Geol. Mag.*, vol. lxxv, 1938, p. 507.

GRANULITES, SCHISTS, PARAGNEISSES, ETC.

760. Granulite. Central Psammitic Gneiss in core of Morar anticline (' Sub-Moine '). W. side of Rudha Dubh, 673 yd S. 49° E. of Bracorina School, North Morar, Inverness-shire. 1-in. 61 Scot., 6-in. 106 S.E. (1053. Anal., C. O. Harvey).

S 32732. A pale pinkish-grey rock with irregular green bands. Microscopically it is composed of an aggregate of interlocking granulitized quartz, albite, ortho-clase and microcline grains, tablets of muscovite and biotite arranged in a parallel fashion, plentiful iron ore and epidote crystals and small sphene granules. Orthite sometimes forms cores to the epidote crystals.

761. Granulite. Upper Psammitic Group of Morar, Moine Series. Point of promontory, Loch Sunart, 1000 yd S. 30° W. of Glenmore, Ardnamurchan, Argyllshire. 1-in. 52 Scot., 6-in. 25 S.E. (1079. Anal., G. A. Sergeant).
S 33790. A fine pebbly pinkish-brown rock containing coarse grains of granulitized quartz and microcline in an irregular mosaic of finer-grained quartz, microcline, orthoclase and microperthite. The quartz is riddled with minute inclusions. Muscovite flakes, displaying a rude foliation, are plentiful and iron ore and epidote granules are common. There is a little biotite, secondary chlorite and accessory apatite, sphene and tourmaline.

762. Pyroxene-anorthite-zoisite-granulite. Calc-silicate band in Striped Group of Moine Series. 1630 yd E. 10° S. of General Ross's Cairn, 100 yd S. 20° W. of Dalelia Mica Prospect, Moidart, Inverness-shire. 1-in. 52 Scot., 6-in. 157 N.E. (1379. Anal., G. A. Sergeant).
S 35717. A pink and pale-green rock composed of irregular colourless pyroxene prisms and large allotriomorphic garnets in a groundmass of quartz and anorthite with accessory granular sphene. Prisms of zoisite are plentiful.
Geol. Mag., vol. lxxxvi, 1949, p. 47.

	GRANULITES, ETC.				
	760	761	762	763	764
SiO_2.. ..	83·39	82·01	73·51	72·57	65·70
Al_2O_3 ..	7·53	8·77	12·21	13·04	14·24
Fe_2O_3 ..	1·51	0·98	0·44	0·31	1·51
FeO	0·76	0·57	2·05	2·84	6·37
MgO ..	0·31	0·17	0·59	0·67	4·89
CaO ..	0·90	0·48	9·52	1·36	2·39
Na_2O ..	1·20	1·14	0·21	3·07	1·96
K_2O ..	3·22	4·71	0·05	4·97	0·27
$H_2O>105°C$	0·47	0·50	0·27	0·26	1·60
$H_2O<105°C$	0·04	0·04	0·06	0·05	0·13
TiO_2 ..	0·48	0·31	0·54	0·62	0·94
P_2O_5 ..	0·04	0·03	0·11	0·13	0·17
MnO ..	0·06	0·02	0·44	0·04	0·09
CO_2.. ..	tr.	0·20	0·06	tr.	tr.
Cl	—	tr.	tr.	—	—
F	—	—	—	—	—
S	tr.	n.d.	0·02	—	—
FeS_2 ..	—	—	—	0·08	—
Fe_7S_8 ..	—	—	—	tr.	—
Cr_2O_3 ..	—	tr.	n.d.	0·01	0·01
BaO ..	0·07	0·12	n.d.	0·05	0·02
SrO	—	—	—	—	—
Li_2O ..	—	—	tr.	—	—
Rb_2O ..	—	—	—	—	—
TOTAL	99·98	100·05	100·08	100·07	100·29
Sp. gr. ..	2·69	—	—	—	2·775

763. Augen-gneiss. Injection-rock of Moine Series (pegmatite-injected mica-schist). Strontian River, 200 yd downstream from junction with Allt Feith Dhomhnuill, Sunart, Argyllshire. 1-in. 52 Scot., 6-in. 18 S.E. (975. Anal., C. O. Harvey).
S 30276. A coarse grey rock in which plentiful biotite is arranged in coarse folia around allotriomorphic quartz, perthite, oligoclase and subordinate myrmekite grains. There is a little muscovite· and apatite, garnet and zircon are accessory.
S.P. 1934, Pt. I (1935), p. 83.

764. Anthophyllite-cordierite-granulite. Gneiss of Lizard Complex, pre-Devonian. 250 yd N. of Trelease Mill, St. Keverne, Cornwall. 1-in. 359, 6-in. 81 N.W. (982. Anal., C. O. Harvey).
E 17043. A dark-grey rock composed of granulitized porphyroblasts of cordierite set in a mosaic of quartz, andesine and cordierite, with elongate prisms of anthophyllite, biotite tablets occurring in bands, iron ore and small needles of sillimanite.
S.P. 1935, Pt. I (1936), p. 93. *Geol. Mag.*, vol. lxxiv, 1937, p. 304. *M.G.S.* ' Lizard ', 2nd edit., 1946, p. 43.
See also No. **752.**

765. Feldspar-blebbed gneiss. Westing Group, Shetland Metamorphic Series. 660 yd S.W. of Lund farmhouse, Unst, Shetland. 1-in. 131 Scot., 6-in. 8 N.W. (934. Anal., B. E. Dixon).
S 29293. A dark-grey rock in which coarse crystals of zoned andesine, often sheathed in muscovite and biotite, are set in a base of granulitized oligoclase and quartz with abundant irregular muscovite and biotite, prisms of epidote and accessory iron ore and apatite.
S.P. 1932, Pt. I (1933), p. 96. *Min. Mag.*, vol. xxiii, 1934, p. 533.

766. Calc-zoisite-biotite-garnet-granulite. Calc-silicate bands in Upper Striped Group of Moine Series. Shore, N.E. side of Mallaig Harbour, North Morar, Invernessshire. 1-in. 61 Scot., 6-in. 106 N.W. (1054. Anal., C. O. Harvey).
S 33239-56. A composite sample from 18 separate bands. The rocks are of pale greenish-grey colour with small brown garnets and are all very similar. They are composed of quartz and feldspar, mainly albite or oligoclase, with spongy garnets, abundant small prisms of zoisite and flakes of biotite. Sphene, apatite and calcite are present in subordinate amount. The constituents show some variation in their proportions in the different specimens.
Geol. Mag., vol. lxxxvi, 1949, p. 47.

767. Chlorite-muscovite-schist. Retrograde gneiss of Valla Field Group, Shetland Metamorphic Series. 100 yd W. of Gunnister, Unst, Shetland. 1-in. 131 Scot., 6-in. 8 N.W. (936. Anal., B. E. Dixon).
S 29295. A foliated grey schist containing coarse irregular crystals of staurolite.

		SCHISTS, ETC.			
	765	766	767	768	769
SiO_2	64·46	62·73	59·97	58·77	58·39
Al_2O_3	14·60	16·69	21·25	19·69	23·54
Fe_2O_3	2·19	0·42	4·91	0·88	2·43
FeO	4·36	3·02	2·95	6·88	5·16
MgO	2·78	1·09	2·12	2·43	1·88
CaO	3·50	8·86	0·49	1·61	0·33
Na_2O	2·62	2·88	1·39	1·95	1·07
K_2O	3·31	0·90	2·92	3·68	2·90
$H_2O > 105°C$	0·67	0·94	2·54	2·20	2·82
$H_2O < 105°C$	0·04	0·10	0·15	0·12	0·12
TiO_2	1·18	0·67	1·30	1·17	1·22
P_2O_5	0·32	0·31	0·30	0·31	0·07
MnO	0·10	0·29	0·10	0·07	0·02
CO_2	tr.	0·98	tr.	—	tr.
S	—	tr.	—	—	—
FeS_2	tr.	—	—	tr.	tr.
Cr_2O_3	—	—	—	0·01	tr.
BaO	—	0·02	—	0·08	—
TOTAL	100·13	99·90	100·39	99·85	99·95

The base is composed of quartz and muscovite and contains folia of chlorite. There are scarce prisms of chloritoid and accessory iron ore and kyanite. *Q.J.G.S.*, vol. xc, 1934, p. 651.

768. **Garnet-sillimanite-staurolite-mica-schist** (pelitic schist). Band in Moine Schists. 1700 yd N. 15° W. of Dalelia, Loch Shiel, Moidart, Inverness-shire. 1-in. 52 Scot., 6-in. 157 N.E. (973. Anal., C. O. Harvey).
S 30272. A banded grey schist composed of a mosaic of quartz and oligoclase, on which small biotite crystals are moulded. Some bands rich in muscovite contain prisms of staurolite and sheaves of sillimanite needles. Garnet, iron ore and apatite are present in small amount.
S.P. 1934, Pt. I (1935), p. 83.

769. **Chloritoid-muscovite-schist.** Lambhoga Group, Shetland Metamorphic Series. 600 yd S. 20° E. of trigonometrical height 345, Gallow Hill, Fetlar, Shetland. 1-in. 130 Scot., 6-in. 17 N.W. (923. Anal., B. E. Dixon).
S 28614. A banded grey and buff rock composed of lenticular aggregates of granulitized quartz cemented by folia of muscovite. Coarse irregular prisms of chloritoid, often poikiloblastically enclosing other minerals, lie at all angles to the foliation but tend to occur in bands. Chlorite is often intergrown with muscovite and granular leucoxene.
S.P. 1932, Pt. I (1933), p. 95.

770. **Garnetiferous mica-schist** (pelitic schist). Band in Moine Schists. 170 yd W. 10° S. of S. end of Loch Blain, N. of New Shiel Bridge, Moidart, Inverness-shire. 1-in. 52 Scot., 6-in. 157 N.W. (974. Anal., C. O. Harvey).
S 30275. A grey foliated and schistose rock composed of numerous garnets, sometimes well rounded and sheathed in muscovite, biotite and chlorite, in a base of granular quartz and oligoclase with abundant folia of muscovite, biotite and chlorite. Iron ore and apatite are accessory.
S.P. 1934, Pt. I (1935), p. 83.

		SCHISTS AND PARAGNEISSES			
	770	771	772	773	774
SiO_2	58·29	55·79	55·38	55·31	55·09
Al_2O_3	19·53	25·17	12·33	20·71	25·07
Fe_2O_3	1·02	7·07	4·94	0·40*	2·97
FeO	6·85	2·53	3·58	7·64*	5·78
MgO	2·24	1·93	10·32	2·54	1·53
CaO	2·30	0·68	6·28	1·72	0·30
Na_2O	2·25	1·12	1·36	2·45	1·23
K_2O	3·59	3·00	0·68	3·54	2·90
$H_2O > 105°C$	2·00	1·29	3·35	1·39	3·64
$H_2O < 105°C$	0·08	0·10	0·27	0·14	0·06
TiO_2	1·13	1·51	1·07	1·54	1·08
P_2O_5	0·31	0·04	0·12	0·07	0·19
MnO	0·13	0·10	0·13	0·13	0·16
CO_2	—	n.d.	0·24	tr.	tr.
FeS_2	tr.	—	0·10	1·36	tr.
Fe_7S_8	—	—	—	0·04	—
Cr_2O_3	0·01	—	0·10	—	0·03
BaO	0·09	—	—	0·09	—
C	—	—	—	1·10	—
TOTAL	99·82	100·33	100·25	100·17	100·03
Sp. gr.	—	—	—	2·83	—

* Figures approximate owing to presence of carbonaceous matter.

771. Garnet-staurolite-kyanite-gneiss. Valla Field Group, Shetland Metamorphic Series. Cliff top, 490 yd N. 35° W. of trigonometrical height 558, Libbers Hill, Unst, Shetland. 1-in. 131 Scot., 6-in. 2 S.W. (932. Anal., B. E. Dixon).
S 29291. A coarsely foliated rock composed of very coarse prisms of staurolite, irregular rounded garnets and prisms of kyanite in a granulitized mosaic of quartz and oligoclase with abundant robust tablets of muscovite and subordinate biotite. Iron ore and chlorite are present in small amount. The staurolite, kyanite and garnet poikiloblastically enclose quartz and iron ore.
S.P. 1932, Pt. I (1933), p. 96. *Min. Mag.*, vol. xxiii, 1934, p. 533. *Q.J.G.S.*, vol. xc, 1934, p. 651.

772. Epidotic schistose grit. Bed of green schist in Funzie Conglomerate, Shetland Metamorphic Series. Cliff top at The Tind, Fetlar, Shetland. 1-in. 130 Scot., 6-in. 18 N.W. (924. Anal., B. E. Dixon).
S 28615. A greenish-grey finely schistose rock in which scattered grains of quartz lie in a fine-grained groundmass of quartz, abundant granular epidote, greenish biotite flakes, sheaves of chlorite flakes, clear calcite, prisms of pale amphibole and granular iron ore.
S.P. 1932, Pt. I (1933), p. 95.

773. Sillimanite-gneiss. Moine Series. E. side of Beinn Gäire, 1530 yd W. 40° N. of N. end of Lochan Dubh, Moidart, Inverness-shire. 1-in. 52 Scot., 6-in. 149 N.E. (1017. Anal., C. O. Harvey).
S 31737. A dark-grey rock composed of small garnets, dark-brown biotite forming robust tablets which tend to occur in aggregates, knots of sillimanite often in nearly parallel orientation and intergrown with biotite, iron ore including pyrite, and carbonaceous material, with a groundmass of quartz, oligoclase and myrmekite.
S.P. 1937 (1938), p. 96.

774. Chloritoid-schist, ' ottrelite-schist·'. Shetland Metamorphic Series. Shore, Hoswick, Dunrossness, Shetland. 1-in. 126 Scot., 6-in. 62 S.E. (914. Anal., B. E. Dixon).
S 38620. A grey schistose rock composed of prisms and aggregates of chloritoid in a groundmass having a corrugated schistosity and composed of quartz, muscovite, chlorite and granular iron ore.
S.P. 1931, Pt. I (1932), p. 80.

775. Garnet-staurolite-schist. Shetland Metamorphic Series. 450 yd S.S.E. of S. end of Lamba Water, and 1230 yd W.N.W. of West Setter, Weisdale, Shetland. 1-in. 128 Scot., 6-in. 43 S.W. (967. Anal., B. E. Dixon).
S 30032. A grey schistose rock studded with staurolite and garnet, microscopically composed of idiomorphic garnets and coarse prisms of staurolite in a base of coarse-grained muscovite and biotite folia, granular quartz, oligoclase and accessory iron ore. The staurolite diablastically encloses quartz.
S.P. 1934, Pt. I (1935), p. 83.

776. Chloritoid-gneiss (altered andalusite-kyanite-gneiss). Shetland Metamorphic Series. Hillside, 60 yd S.E. of Coubal, Scousburgh, Dunrossness, Shetland. 1-in. 126 Scot., 6-in. 65 N.W. (966. Anal., B. E. Dixon).
S 30031. A grey, rudely banded rock composed of aggregates of robust prisms of chloritoid in a groundmass of fine-grained muscovite, chlorite, quartz and granular ore. Some coarse, more quartzose, areas are also present. There are scarce prisms of andalusite and a little prismatic staurolite.
S.P. 1934, Pt. I (1935), p. 83.

777. Graphitic siliceous schist. Shetland Metamorphic Series. Burn of Vestavirdin, ¾ mile W. of Sullom, Northmaven, Shetland. 1-in. 128 Scot., 6-in. 24 S.E. (964. Anal., B. E. Dixon).
S 30029. A dark-grey rock containing contorted muscovite folia traversing a granular aggregate of quartz and subordinate orthoclase. Opaque ore including coarsely granular pyrrhotite is plentiful and there are many fine-grained graphite aggregates.
S.P. 1934, Pt. I (1935), p. 83.

	SCHISTS AND PARAGNEISS				
	775	776	777	778	779
SiO_2 ..	54·13	53·45	53·0	50·88	49·53
Al_2O_3 ..	27·02	25·34	19·5	31·89	26·06
Fe_2O_3 ..	5·12	6·32	0·2*	2·59	3·00
FeO	2·95	2·42	7·9*	3·48	7·78
MgO ..	1·95	1·49	5·0	1·10	2·59
CaO ..	0·86	1·00	1·1	1·31	1·06
Na_2O ..	1·64	2·09	2·0	1·28	1·03
K_2O ..	2·86	3·43	2·3	2·92	3·78
$H_2O > 105°C$	1·69	3·04	4·2	3·21	3·09
$H_2O < 105°C$	0·16	0·14	0·2	0·08	0·09
TiO_2 ..	1·23	1·33	1·5	1·38	1·62
P_2O_5 ..	0·30	0·10	tr.	tr.	0·12
MnO ..	0·21	0·05	0·1	0·10	0·17
CO_2	—	tr.	0·7	n.d.	n.d.
FeS_2 ..	0·12	—	1·0	tr.	0·25
Fe_7S_8 ..	—	—	1·5	—	—
Cr_2O_3 ..	0·03	0·02	—	—	—
Li_2O ..	tr.	—	—	—	—
C	—	—	0·3	—	—
TOTAL	100·27	100·22	100·5	100·22	100·17

* Figures approximate owing to presence of sub-graphitic matter.

778. Chloritoid-staurolite-schist. Saxa Vord Group, Shetland Metamorphic Series. Summit of Saxa Vord, Unst, Shetland. 1-in. 131 Scot., 6-in. 2 N.E. (933. Anal., B. E. Dixon).
S 29292. A pale-grey schistose rock containing rather irregular prisms of staurolite in a groundmass of quartz, fine-grained muscovite, prisms of chloritoid and a little iron ore, sphene and chlorite.
Min. Mag., vol. xxiii, 1933, p. 322.

779. Garnet-chloritoid-schist. Valla Field Group, Shetland Metamorphic Series. 650 yd W. 12° N. of Snarravoe, Unst, Shetland. 1-in. 130 Scot., 6-in. 8 N.W. (935. Anal., B. E. Dixon).
S 29294. A grey foliated rock composed of a mosaic of granulitized quartz, abundant coarse flakes of muscovite, large garnets partly replaced by chlorite, chloritoid, quartz and muscovite, prisms of staurolite and chloritoid and coarse kyanite. Iron ore, including pyrite, is accessory.
Q.J.G.S., vol. xc, 1934, p. 651.

METAMORPHIC LIMESTONES, ETC.

780. Dolomitized serpentine. Highland Boundary fault-rock, Highland Border Series (Cambro-Ordovician). 650 yd N. by E. of Balmaha Pier, Stirlingshire. 1-in. 38 Scot., 6-in. 13 S.E. (1343. Anal., C. O. Harvey).
S 35523-6. A yellow, green, red and purple brecciated rock composed of silicified and carbonated serpentine, sometimes preserving original mesh-structure, and sometimes brecciated and cemented by limonite and carbonate. Chromite is present in scattered grains and secondary chlorite and quartz are present. Carbonate is mainly or entirely ankerite.
Geol. Surv. Wartime Pamphlet No. 13, ' Limestones of Scotland. Area V. Central Grampians ', 2nd edit., 1944, p. 17. *Min. Res.*, vol. xxxiv, ' Rock Wool ', 1945, pp. 14, 17; 2nd edit., 1949, pp. 15, 18. *Min. Res.*, vol. xxxv, ' Limestones of Scotland ', 1949, p. 176.

781. Metamorphic limestone. Loch Tay Limestone, Dalradian Series. 750 yd N. of Glendaruel House, Cowall, Argyllshire. 1-in. 29 Scot., 6-in. 162 S.W. (1433. Anal., G. A. Sergeant).
S 35996. A grey laminated crystalline limestone composed of coarse elongate granular calcite grains, plentiful subangular to rounded quartz grains and parallel flakes of white mica. Granular pyrite and leucoxene are present in small quantity and there is also finely divided opaque material.

782. Marble. Mass in Lewisian hornblende-augite-gneiss. Quarry, 92 yd E. 36° S. of Balephetrish, Tiree, Argyllshire. 1-in. 42 Scot., 6-in. 64 N.E. (1011. Anal., C. O. Harvey).
S 31648-9, 31697. A pink and green coccolite-marble containing rounded grains of pale-green pyroxene sometimes intergrown with orthoclase, crystals of scapolite altered to white mica, and occasional coarse calcite grains in a base of very fine-grained calcite. Sphene, apatite and limonitic aggregates are accessory constituents.

	METAMORPHIC LIMESTONES, ETC.				
	780	781	782	783	784
SiO_2 ..	39·1	21·58	8·93	11·12	2·0
Al_2O_3 ..	1·8*	4·66	0·93	1·50	1·0
Fe_2O_3 ..	5·4†	1·16	0·07	0·35	tr.†
FeO	—	—	0·93	0·34	—
MgO ..	12·4	0·79	2·74	1·36	2·2
CaO ..	15·0	37·93	49·02	46·23	51·9
Na_2O ..	—	0·96	0·20	0·23	—
K_2O ..	—	1·13	0·17	0·41	—
$H_2O>105°C$	—	0·56	0·19	0·24	—
$H_2O<105°C$	—	0·07	0·05	0·08	0·1
TiO_2 ..	tr.	0·17	0·08	0·06	—
P_2O_5 ..	tr.	0·06	0·04	0·14	—
MnO ..	0·1*	0·05	0·59	0·07	—
CO_2	—	30·26	36·38	37·34	42·5
SO_3	—	0·02	—	—	—
Cl	—	tr.	—	—	—
S	—	—	0·01	0·29	—
FeS_2 ..	—	0·54	—	—	—
Fe_7S_8 ..	—	tr.	—	—	—
Cr_2O_3 ..	0·3*	—	n.d.	tr.	—
BaO ..	tr.*	—	—	0·03	—
SrO	tr.*	—	—	0·3(s)§	—
C	—	0·17	—	tr.	—
Loss on igni-					
tion ..	25·9	—	—	—	—
TOTAL	100·0‡	100·11	100·33	100·09	—
Sp. gr. ..	—	2·73	2·80	2·73	—

* Approximate figures partly based on spectrographic work.
† Total Fe calculated as Fe_2O_3.
‡ CO_2: 24·7. $H_2O<105°C$: 0·4.
§ Approximate.

783. Metamorphic limestone. Dalradian Series. Most southerly quarry, immediately E. of road, 200 yd S. of school, 3 miles N.W. of Kirkton of Glenbuchat, Aberdeenshire. 1-in. 75 Scot., 6-in. 60 N.W. (1522. Anal., W. F. Waters; spect. det., J. A. C. McClelland).

S 37487. A grey crystalline limestone composed of interlocking calcite crystals of variable grain size, scattered small irregular to rounded quartz grains, and white mica flakes. Scarce pyrite cubes are present.

784. **Metamorphic limestone.** Mass in ' Lewisian Inlier '. N. side of track, 900 yd W. 20° N. of Glendessarry Lodge, Glen Dessarry, Inverness-shire. 1-in. 62 Scot., 6-in. 109 S.W. (1401. Anal., G. A. Sergeant).
S 35893-5. A pale-blue to white rock composed of coarsely crystalline inter-locking calcite grains enclosing small crystals of forsterite, diopside, tremolite, phlogopite and grossular, and accessory sphene, apatite and opaque ore.
Min. Res., vol. xxv, ' Limestones of Scotland ', 1949, p. 35.

HORNFELSES, ETC.

785. **Biotite-cordierite-hornfels.** Metamorphosed Skiddaw Slate (Ordovician) from aureole of Skiddaw Granite (probably Old Red Sandstone). River Caldew, 300 yd below its junction with Grainsgill Beck, Cumberland. 1-in. 23, 6-in. 48 S.W. (1012. Anal., C. O. Harvey).
E 17441. A striped dark-grey spotted hornfels composed of abundant scattered biotite flakes in a groundmass partly of coarse-grained cordierite and partly of bands of fine angular quartz with abundant fine-grained muscovite. Opaque ore is present in abundant small rods and granules in the cordierite. The rock is traversed by scarce veinlets of quartz.
S.P. 1937 (1938), p. 96.

786. **Andalusite-cordierite-hornfels.** Metamorphosed Skiddaw Slate (Ordovician) from aureole of Skiddaw Granite (probably Old Red Sandstone). 200 yd S. of outlet of Bowscale Tarn, Caldew Valley, Cumberland. 1-in. 23, 6-in. 57 N.W. (1013. Anal., C. O. Harvey).
E 17442. A dark-grey spotted hornfels composed of porphyroblasts of cor-dierite and andalusite (often chiastolite) with abundant poikiloblastic biotite in a matrix of fine-grained white mica, chlorite, cordierite, a little quartz, granular iron ore including pyrite and ilmenite, and fine-grained carbonaceous matter. Zircon and tourmaline are accessory.
S.P. 1937 (1938), p. 96.

787. **Cordierite-biotite-hornfels.** Metamorphosed Skiddaw Slate (Ordovician) from aureole of Skiddaw Granite (probably Old Red Sandstone). 30 yd N.W. of Lead Mine hut, Bannerdale, 1⅘ miles W. 17° S. of Mungrisdale, Cumberland. 1-in. 23, 6-in. 57 N.W. (1014. Anal., C. O. Harvey).
E 17443. A dark-grey spotted hornfels containing cordierite porphyroblasts, evenly scattered biotite and abundant fine-grained white mica with iron ore including pyrite in strings of granules. Carbonaceous matter is very finely dis-seminated.
S.P. 1937 (1938), p. 96.

788. **Thomsonite-pyroxene-garnet-rock.** Enclosure in picrite in sill (probably Car-boniferous) in Oil-shale Group of Calciferous Sandstone Series (Carboniferous). 367 ft deep, Blackness No. 2 Borehole, ½ mile W. of Blackness Castle, Linlith-gowshire. 1-in. 32 Scot., 6-in. 2 S.W. (919. Anal., B. E. Dixon).
S 27948, 28309. A greenish-grey ophimottled rock composed of coarse crystals of thomsonite in which are embedded abundant small stumpy prisms of greenish pyroxene often clustered around clear spots, scattered idiomorphic grossular crystals, idiomorphic individuals of sphene and plentiful iron ore including pyrite in part forming pseudomorphs with a chloritic mineral. Analcite and albite are present in small quantity and there are accessory apatite and zircon and a little carbonate, chlorite and fibrous amphibole.
S.P. 1931, Pt. I (1932), p. 80. *S.P.* 1933, Pt. II (1934), p. 87.

	HORNFELSES, ETC.				PORCEL-LANITE	APATITE-ROCK
	785	786	787	788	789	790
SiO_2	63·18	56·19	55·25	39·82	35·73	8·8
Al_2O_3	19·29	22·48	22·38	14·72	32·69	1·1
Fe_2O_3	0·27	0·58*	0·72*	2·21	26·45	1·7
FeO	6·55	7·65*	8·59*	5·28	1·03	0·9
MgO	1·86	1·93	2·06	7·30	0·35	1·6
CaO	0·46	0·61	0·82	13·32	0·07	45·7
Na_2O	1·04	1·06	1·08	2·63	0·15	0·2
K_2O	3·81	3·34	2·70	0·34	0·07	0·1
$H_2O > 105°C$	2·12	3·37	3·49	6·93	0·67	—
$H_2O < 105°C$	0·19	0·44	0·50	2·79	0·27	—
TiO_2	0·98	1·21	1·12	0·99	2·12	0·4
P_2O_5	0·11	0·28	0·13	1·01	0·05	30·3
MnO	0·10	0·07	0·54	0·22	0·06	0·1
CO_2	0·02	0·01	0·02	0·53	tr.	3·7
SO_3	—	—	—	—	—	1·4
Cl	—	—	—	—	—	0·3
F	—	—	—	—	—	1·4
S	—	—	—	—	0·02	—
FeS_2	0·05	0·32	0·12	1·72	—	—
Fe_7S_8	0·03	0·24	0·54	tr.	—	—
Cr_2O_3	0·01	0·01	0·01	0·07	0·41	—
BaO	0·05	0·05	0·03	—	0·02	0·6
SrO	—	—	—	—	—	0·4
Li_2O	—	—	—	—	0·0008(s)	—
Rb_2O	—	—	—	—	tr. (<0·001;s)	—
Cs_2O	—	—	—	—	n.d. (<0·01;s)	—
C	—	0·20	0·13	—	—	—
Loss on ignition	—	—	—	—	—	1·4‡
TOTAL	100·12	100·04	100·23	99·88	100·16†	100·1
Less O for Cl,F	—	—	—	—	—	0·7
	100·12	100·04	100·23	99·88	100·16	99·4
Sp. gr.	2·76	2·79	2·77	—	3·24	—

* Approximate owing to presence of sulphides and carbonaceous matter.
† Vanadium about 0·05(s).
‡ Less CO_2.

789. Porcellanite. Scree material from contact-altered rock; probably a metamorphosed lithomarge from the Tertiary Interbasaltic Horizon. Tievebulliagh, 2½ miles W.S.W. of Cushendall, Co. Antrim. 1-in. 14 Ire., 6-in. 19 N.E. (1615. Anal., A. D. Wilson, K. L. H. Murray and P. Coombs; spect. det., C. O. Harvey and K. L. H. Murray).
N I 310. A dark-grey mottled rock composed of aggregates of opaque to deep-red haematite cemented by quartz and set in a very fine-grained felt of needles of sillimanite.
Ulster Journ. Archaeology, vol. xv, 1952 (1953), p. 58. *S.P.* 1952 (1953), p. 49.

790. Apatite-rock. Vertical lenticular mass in ash-vent, Ordovician. Bank of dry gully, 630 yd S. of Guffock Hill, W. of Bail Hill, near Sanquhar, Dumfriesshire. 1-in. 15 Scot., 6-in. 6 N.W. (994. Anal., C. O. Harvey).
S 31276. A medium-brown apatite-rock composed of abundant robust idio-morphic prisms of apatite ($\omega = 1 \cdot 637$, $\varepsilon = 1 \cdot 634$) up to about $0 \cdot 8$ mm in length, cemented by finely granular calcite in which are set numerous flakes of reddish-brown phlogopite, scarce irregular crystals of baryte and granules of iron ore. There are rare grains of quartz.
S.P. 1935, Pt. II (1937), p. 56.
See also Nos. **813-4.**

SLATES

791. Clay (altered slate). Altered wall rock (Lower Devonian) of Perran Iron Lode (oxidized siderite with pyrite; Permo-Carboniferous). 400 yd S.E. of Treamble cross-roads, 550 yd N. of Hendra, 1¼ miles S. by E. of Cubert Church, Corn-wall. 1-in. 346, 6-in. 48 N.W. (1598. Anal., W. F. Waters and P. Coombs; spect. det., C. O. Harvey and K. L. H. Murray).
E 24721. A white altered slate, ranging from a soft clay to a friable slate, com-posed of folia of white mica arranged with uniform orientation, kaolin and granulitized quartz partly in coarse grains and partly in re-cemented lenticles. Occasional narrow dark streaks are partly biotite and partly leucoxene.
S.P. 1951 (1953), p. 63.
See also No. **799.**

792. Slate. Ballachulish Slates, Dalradian Series. Main Ballachulish Slate Quarry, Argyllshire. 1-in. 53 Scot., 6-in. 30 S.E. (1374. Anal., C. O. Harvey and G. A. Sergeant; spect. det., J. A. C. McClelland).
S 35712. A grey slate composed of a schistose aggregate of quartz silt, chlorite, white mica and fine-grained opaque granules. The quartz forms occasional nodular aggregates, and there are common small chloritic knots, crystals of pyrite and aggregates of leucoxene.

793. Slate. Easdale Slates, Dalradian Series. Cullipool Slate Quarry, Luing, Argyll-shire. 1-in. 36 Scot., 6-in. 129 N.E. (1377. Anal., C. O. Harvey and G. A. Sergeant; spect. det., J. A. C. McClelland).
S 35715. A foliated grey slate having lenticles and laminae which are sometimes rich in quartz and sometimes composed mainly of chlorite, white mica and fine opaque granules and films possibly in part carbonaceous. There are occasional quartz porphyroblasts that are penetrated by the foliation laminae of muscovite and chlorite and associated with traces of pyrite.

794. Slate. Ballachulish Slates, Dalradian Series. Main Ballachulish Slate Quarry, Argyllshire. 1-in. 53 Scot., 6-in. 30 S.E. (1375. Anal., C. O. Harvey and G. A. Sergeant; spect. det., J. A. C. McClelland).
S 35713. A grey slate composed of a schistose aggregate of quartz silt, chlorite, white mica and fine-grained opaque granules. The quartz tends to form lenticles and there are numerous nodular quartz aggregates. Small pyrite crystals and leucoxene aggregates are common.

795. Slate. Skiddaw Slate, Ordovician. 1470 yd W. 43° S. of Mungrisdale Church, Cumberland. 1-in. 23, 6-in. 57 N.W. (1036. Anal., C. O. Harvey).
E 17555. A striped grey slate composed of flakes and rosettes of white mica in a base of pale-green chlorite and perhaps kaolin with very fine-grained opaque material. Adjacent laminae have varying proportions of these constituents; cleavage traces nearly perpendicular to the laminae are depicted in opaque, probably carbonaceous, matter.
S.P. 1937 (1938), p. 96.

	SLATES				
	791	792	793	794	795
SiO$_2$	69·35	62·6	61·8	59·4	58·41
Al$_2$O$_3$	20·38	18·0	16·2	20·0	20·25
Fe$_2$O$_3$	0·31	6·9*	7·3*	6·7*	0·63†
FeO	0·12	—	—	—	8·05†
MgO	0·44	3·2	2·6	3·0	2·02
CaO	0·08	0·1	0·4	0·1	0·41
Na$_2$O	0·19	1·1	1·6	1·1	0·68
K$_2$O	3·67	2·9	2·7	3·4	2·50
H$_2$O>105°C	4·42	—	—	—	4·87
H$_2$O<105°C	0·29	—	—	—	0·46
TiO$_2$	0·85	0·8	0·9	0·8	1·00
P$_2$O$_5$	0·05	0·1	0·2	0·1	0·23
MnO	0·01	tr.(s)	tr.(s)	tr.(s)	0·07
CO$_2$	n.d.	—	—	—	—
SO$_3$	—	—	—	—	—
S	0·02	—	—	—	tr.
Cr$_2$O$_3$	0·02	tr.(s)	tr.(s)	tr.(s)	—
BaO	0·04	tr.(s)	tr.(s)	tr.(s)	0·04
SrO	—	tr.(s)	tr.(s)	tr.(s)	—
Li$_2$O	0·01(s)	n.d.	n.d.	n.d.	—
Rb$_2$O	0·02(s)	—	—	—	—
Cs$_2$O	n.d. (<0·02; s)	—	—	—	—
C	—	—	—	—	0·39
Loss on ignition	—	4·1	6·2	4·7	—
TOTAL	100·27	99·8‡	99·9§	99·3‖	100·01
Add SO$_3$ retained during ignition	—	tr.	0·1	0·3	—
	100·27	99·8	100·0	99·6	100·01
Sp. gr.	2·72	—	—	—	2·77

* Total Fe calculated as Fe$_2$O$_3$.
† Figures approximate owing to carbonaceous matter.
‡ H$_2$O<105°C: 0·1. CO$_2$: 0·1. SO$_3$: n.d. S: 0·3. C: 0·5.
§ H$_2$O<105°C: 0·1. CO$_2$: 3·0. SO$_3$: n.d. S: 0·9. C: 0·2.
‖ H$_2$O<105°C: 0·1. CO$_2$: 0·1. SO$_3$: n.d. S: 0·5. C: 0·6.

796. Slate. Aberfoyle Slates, Dalradian Series. Aberfoyle Slate Quarry, 1¾ miles N.W. of Aberfoyle, Perthshire. 1-in. 38 Scot., 6-in. 122 S.E. (1378. Anal., C. O. Harvey and G. A. Sergeant; spect. det., J. A. C. McClelland).
S 35716. A foliated grey slate having laminae and lenticles containing different proportions of quartz silt, chlorite, muscovite, opaque granules and carbonaceous films. Apatite and tourmaline prisms and grains of albite are accessory.

797. Slate. Altered Skiddaw Slate (Ordovician), adjacent to a small basic intrusion. 220 yd S. 9° W. of Barkbeth, Bassenthwaite, Cumberland. 1-in. 23, 6-in. 56 N.W. (1035. Anal., C. O. Harvey).
E 17554. A pale-grey slate containing a clathrate mesh of spots of chlorite in a groundmass of white mica, interstitial yellow-stained material (perhaps chlorite)

and granules of iron ore. There are numerous quartz grains and the rock is traversed by veinlets of quartz with radiating chlorite.

S.P. 1937 (1938), p. 96.

See also No. **798.**

798. Slate. Skiddaw Slate (Ordovician), 40 yd from contact of basic intrusion and altered slate No. **797.** 200 yd S. 16° W. of Barkbeth, Bassenthwaite, Cumberland. 1-in. 23, 6-in. 56 N.W. (1034. Anal., C. O. Harvey).

E 17553. A grey slate composed of pale chlorite often forming small aggregates, finely divided white mica arranged in a well-foliated manner, fine carbonaceous streaks and a little angular quartz silt.

S.P. 1937 (1938), p. 96.

	SLATES				
	796	797	798	799	800
SiO_2 ..	56·5	55·45	54·95	54·28	52·6
Al_2O_3 ..	19·6	23·29	24·33	24·70	14·3
Fe_2O_3 ..	9·9*	0·70	0·60‡	3·22	6·2*
FeO	—	6·26	7·04‡	4·07	—
MgO ..	2·5	2·45	1·85	1·41	8·0
CaO ..	0·8	0·40	0·36	0·03	1·6
Na_2O ..	3·0	0·71	0·98	1·18	1·6
K_2O ..	2·9	3·96	3·02	4·50	2·3
$H_2O>105°C$	—	5·10	5·32	4·98	—
$H_2O<105°C$	—	0·35	0·69	0·42	—
TiO_2 ..	1·4	1·07	1·07	1·04	0·6
P_2O_5 ..	0·2	0·20	0·11	0·03	0·1
MnO ..	tr.(s)	0·20	0·42	0·11	tr.(s)
CO_2	—	—	—	0·01	—
S	—	tr.	tr.	0·02	—
Cr_2O_3 ..	tr.(s)	—	—	0·02	tr.(s)
BaO ..	tr.(s)	0·09	0·05	0·06	tr.(s)
SrO	tr.(s)	—	—	—	tr.(s)
Li_2O ..	n.d.	—	—	0·02(s)	tr.
Rb_2O ..	—	—	—	0·02(s)	—
Cs_2O ..	—	—	—	n.d. (<0·02; s)	—
C	—	0·02	0·39	—	—
Loss on ignition ..	3·2	—	—	—	11·5
TOTAL	100·0†	100·25	100·18	100·12	98·8§
Add SO_3 retained during ignition ..	—	—	—	—	0·9
	100·0	100·25	100·18	100·12	99·7
Sp. gr. ..	—	. 2·79	2·77	2·82	—

* Total Fe calculated as Fe_2O_3.

† $H_2O<105°C$: 0·2. CO_2: 0·1. SO_3: n.d. S: n.d. C: tr.

‡ Figures approximate owing to carbonaceous matter.

§ $H_2O<105°C$: 0·1. CO_2: 7·9. SO_3: tr. S: 1·0. C: 0·8.

799. Slate. Lower Devonian. Wall rock of Perran Iron Lode (oxidized siderite with pyrite; Permo-Carboniferous), 15 ft from apparent limit of alteration. 400 yd S.E. of Treamble cross-roads, 550 yd N. of Hendra, 1¼ miles S. by E. of Cubert

Church, Cornwall. 1-in. 346, 6-in. 48 N.W. (1597. Anal., W. F. Waters and P. Coombs).
E 24720. An iron-stained slate composed of a compact orientated mass of white mica, sometimes forming plates extinguishing uniformly, kaolin, lenticles of granulitized quartz and films and veinlets of limonite. Cleavage in two directions intersecting at low angles is depicted by folia of fine opaque granular material, possibly ferruginous.
S.P. 1951 (1953), p. 63.
See also No. **791.**

800. **Slate.** Easdale Slates, Dalradian Series. Balvicar Slate Quarry, Seil, Argyllshire, 1-in. 36 Scot., 6-in. 121 S.E. (1376. Anal., C. O. Harvey and G. A. Sergeant; spect. det., J. A. C. McClelland).
S 35714. A dark-grey slate composed of quartz and ankerite, of silt grade, in grains elongated along a well-developed cleavage, cemented by chlorite, clay-mica and finely divided opaque matter. There is a little dolomite and scarce pyrite.

IV. PARTIAL ANALYSES OF METAMORPHIC ROCKS

801. Quartzite. Scaraben Quartzite, Moine Series. Near summit of Beinn Dubhain, Kildonan, Sutherland. 1-in. 109 Scot., 6-in. 78 N.E. (1087. Anal., C. O. Harvey and G. A. Sergeant). S 34070.
Geol. Surv. Wartime Pamphlet No. 7, ' High-grade Silica Rocks of the Scottish Highlands and Islands ', 1st edit., 1940, p. 3; 2nd edit., 1945, p. 6.
SiO_2: 99·27%. Al_2O_3: 0·26%. Total Fe calculated as Fe_2O_3: 0·10%. MgO: 0·02%. CaO: 0·01%. Na_2O: 0·02%. K_2O: 0·06%. TiO_2: 0·03%. P_2O_5: 0·01%. Loss on ignition: 0·10%.

802. Quartzite. Bulk sample representing 27 ft of rock. Binnein Quartzite, Dalradian Series. Crags above road to Mamore Lodge, 250 yd N.E. of junction with road along N. side of Loch Leven, Inverness-shire. 1-in. 53 Scot., 6-in. 167 N.W. (1394. Anal., G. A. Sergeant). S 35817-9.
Geol. Surv. Wartime Pamphlet No. 7, ' High-grade Silica Rocks of the Scottish Highlands and Islands ', 2nd edit., 1945, p. 24.
SiO_2: 99·1%. Total Fe calculated as Fe_2O_3: 0·08%. Na_2O: 0·02%. K_2O: 0·11%. $H_2O < 105°C$: 0·01%.

803. Quartzite. Bulk sample representing 15 ft of rock. Binnein Quartzite, Dalradian Series. Crags on hillside just E. of Allt Coire an Eich, $1\frac{1}{2}$ miles W. by S. of Kinlochleven, Argyllshire. 1-in. 53 Scot., 6-in. 31 N.E. (1392. Anal., G. A Sergeant). S 35809-13.
Geol. Surv. Wartime Pamphlet No. 7, ' High-grade Silica Rocks of the Scottish Highlands and Islands ', 2nd edit., 1945, p. 24.
SiO_2: 98·5%. Total Fe calculated as Fe_2O_3: 0·09%. Na_2O: n.d. K_2O: 0·23%. $H_2O < 105°C$: 0·04%.

804. Quartzite. Bulk sample representing 44 ft of rock. Binnein Quartzite, Dalradian Series. Roadside crags opposite low water mark at head of Loch Leven, Inverness-shire. 1-in. 53 Scot., 6-in. 167 N.W. (1393. Anal., G. A. Sergeant). S 35814-6.
Geol. Surv. Wartime Pamphlet No. 7, ' High-grade Silica Rocks of the Scottish Highlands and Islands ', 2nd edit., 1945, p. 24.
SiO_2: 98·4%. Total Fe calculated as Fe_2O_3: 0·16%. Na_2O: 0·02%. K_2O: 0·25%. $H_2O < 105°C$: 0·03%.

805. Quartzite. Bulk sample representing 24 ft of rock. Binnein Quartzite, Dalradian Series. Crags, $\frac{1}{4}$ mile S. of Caolasnacon, Loch Leven, Argyllshire. 1-in. 53 Scot., 6-in. 31 N.W. (1391. Anal., G. A. Sergeant). S 35805-8.
Geol. Surv. Wartime Pamphlet No. 7, ' High-grade Silica Rocks of the Scottish Highlands and Islands ', 2nd edit., 1945, p. 24.
SiO_2: 97·8%. Total Fe calculated as Fe_2O_3: 0·09%. Na_2O: n.d. K_2O: 0·49%. $H_2O < 105°C$: 0·02%.

806. Dolomite. Appin Limestone, Dalradian Series. In tributary to main stream above West Laroch, 660 yd S. 23° W. of bridge carrying main road over River Laroch, S. of Loch Leven, Argyllshire. 1-in. 53 Scot., 6-in. 30 S.E. (1165. Anal., C. O. Harvey). S 34599.
Total Fe calculated as Fe_2O_3: 1·4%. MgO: 19·9%. CaO: 29·2%. $H_2O < 105°C$: tr. Insoluble residue: 5·0%.

807. Dolomite. Appin Limestone, Dalradian Series. Old quarry, 660 yd E. 20° N. of Dalnatrat road bridge, Salachan Glen, Argyllshire. 1-in. 53 Scot., 6-in. 43 S.E. (1166. Anal., C. O. Harvey). S 34600.
Total Fe calculated as Fe_2O_3: 0·3%. MgO: 20·7%. CaO: 29·4%. $H_2O < 105°C$: 0·1%. Insoluble residue: 4·4%.

808. Contact-metamorphosed greywacke. Adjacent to Newmains Dyke (Lower Old Red Sandstone) intruding Silurian greywackes. Near Newmains, $4\frac{1}{2}$ miles W. of Dumfries and $11\frac{1}{2}$ miles N.E. of Castle Douglas, Kircudbrightshire. 1-in. 9 Scot., 6-in. 29 N.W. (954-5. Anal., B. E. Dixon).

Q.J.G.S., vol. xcii, 1936, p. 122.
954:—Na_2O: 2·68%. K_2O: 3·30%.
955:—Na_2O: 2·77%. K_2O: 3·87%.

809. **Contaminated basalt.** Inclusion of Eycott type big-feldspar basalt in Carrock Fell Gabbro No. 743 (post-Borrowdale Volcanic Series of Ordovician, probably Old Red Sandstone). Crag, 770 yd N. 36° W. of Mosedale Bridge over River Caldew, Mosedale, Cumberland. 1-in. 23, 6-in. 48 S.W. (1558. Anal., K. L. H. Murray). E. 23494.
Na_2O: 3·53%. K_2O: 1·45%.
See also No. 744.

810. **Garnet-oligoclase-hornfels.** Skiddaw Slate (Ordovician) metamorphosed by Carrock Fell Gabbro (post-Borrowdale Volcanic Series of Ordovician, probably Old Red Sandstone). 1130 yd N. 55° W. of Mosedale Bridge over River Caldew, Mosedale, Cumberland. 1-in. 23, 6-in. 48 S.W. (1569. Anal., K. L. H. Murray). E 23496.
Na_2O: 1·29%. K_2O: 4·12%. Li_2O: tr.
See also No. 875.

811. **Quartz-albite-chlorite-hornfels.** Skiddaw Slate (Ordovician) metamorphosed by Carrock Fell Gabbro (post-Borrowdale Volcanic Series of Ordovician, probably Old Red Sandstone). 600 yd N. 10° W. of Swineside, Cumberland. 1-in. 23, 6-in. 48 S.W. (1570. Anal., K. L. H. Murray). E 23508.
Na_2O: 2·06%. K_2O: 2·98%. Li_2O: tr.

812. **Biotite-oligoclase-hornfels.** Skiddaw Slate (Ordovician) metamorphosed by Carrock Fell Gabbro and Skiddaw Granite (both probably Old Red Sandstone). Arm o' Grain, 50 yd N. of junction with Grainsgill Beck, S. of High Pike, Cumberland. 1-in. 23, 6-in. 47 S.E. (1571. Anal., K. L. H. Murray). E 23515.
Na_2O: 1·04%. K_2O: 3·97%. Li_2O: tr.

813. **Apatite-rock.** Vertical lenticular mass in ash-vent, Ordovician. Bank of dry gully, 630 yd S. of Guffock Hill, W. of Bail Hill, near Sanquhar, Dumfriesshire. 1-in. 15 Scot., 6-in. 6 N.W. (995. Anal., C. O. Harvey). S 31277.
P_2O_5: 31·2%.
See also Nos. 790, 814.

814. **Apatite-rock.** Vertical lenticular mass in ash-vent, Ordovician. Bank of dry gully, 630 yd S. of Guffock Hill, W. of Bail Hill, near Sanquhar, Dumfriesshire. 1-in. 15 Scot., 6-in. 6 N.W. (996. Anal., C. O. Harvey). S 31278.
P_2O_5: 30·7%.
See also Nos. 790, 813.

	815	816	817	818	819
SiO_2 ..	65·6	0·06	7·23	3·3	6·59
Al_2O_3 ..	5·6	—	0·17	0·5	0·29
Fe_2O_3 ..	2·6	10·2	60·14	84·1§	0·83
FeO	3·6	16·5	28·20	—	5·61
MgO ..	1·0	n.d.	1·40	2·6	41·01
CaO ..	1·0	0·3	2·26	0·2	0·48
Na_2O ..	0·1	0·15	0·10	—	—
K_2O ..	0·3	—	0·20	—	—
$H_2O > 105°C$	8·5	0·05	0·29	—	0·98‖
$H_2O < 105°C$	9·6	—	0·06	0·1	0·18
TiO_2 ..	1·0	54·5	0·42	0·1	tr.
P_2O_5 ..	tr.	—	0·03	n.d.	n.d.
MnO ..	tr.	—	tr.	0·1(s)	0·22
CO_2	n.d.	—	tr.	—	43·99
ZrO_2 ..	—	0·4	—	n.d.	—
SO_3	n.d.	—	—	—	n.d.
S	0·1	—	—	—	—
Cr_2O_3 ..	tr.	0·17	—	10·5	0·16
V_2O_3 ..	—	—	—	0·1(s)	—
V_2O_5 ..	—	1·4	—	—	—
NiO	—	—	—	0·1	0·07
BaO	n.d.	—	—	—	n.d.
SrO	tr.(s)*	—	—	—	—
PbO	0·1(s)*	0·72	—	—	—
ZnO ..	tr.(s)*	—	—	—	—
Li_2O ..	tr.	—	—	—	—
$(Ce, &c.)_2O_3$	—	5·6	—	—	—
U_3O_8 ..	—	9·8	—	—	—
ThO_2 ..	—	0·07	—	—	—
Organic matter	1·1†	—	—	—	—
TOTAL	100·2	99·92‡	100·50	—	100·41

* Approximate figures.
† Calculated from loss on ignition.
‡ Nb_2O_5: n.d. Ta_2O_5: n.d.
§ Total Fe calculated as Fe_2O_3.
‖ Volatile matter other than CO_2 and $H_2O < 105°C$ (largely $H_2O > 105°C$).

815. Opal, impure. Ooliths from chamosite-oolite forming lower part of Cleveland Main Ironstone Seam (Jurassic). Straight West Working, Longacres Mine, Skelton, North Riding, Yorkshire. 1-in. 34, 6-in. 18 N.W. (1481. Anal., C. O. Harvey; spect. det., J. A. C. McClelland. Semi-micro. analysis).
E 21592A. Light concentrate (sp. gr. < 2·64) from ooliths insoluble in cold dilute hydrochloric acid. Some chamosite is present.
M.G.S. ' Liassic Ironstones ', 1952, p. 25; pl. ii, fig. 3.
See also No. 839.

816. Davidite, variety of. From shear zone in noritic country-rock of pre-Karroo age; probably Pre-Cambrian. Mavuzi, Tete district, Mozambique. (Anal., W. Ryan and P. J. Maple, Chemical Research Laboratory).
Ditrigonal pyramidal class (3m) of the trigonal system; mainly massive, or tabular to pyramidal crystals; twinning about the axis [1120]; subconchoidal fracture; hardness=6. Sp. gr.=4·46. Submetallic lustre; grey-black streak and colour. Opaque, except in very thin splinters, where it is translucent and clove-brown; reflectivity for white light (photoelectric cell) 19·5% using galena standard (43·8%).
Min. Mag., vol. xxix, 1950, p. 106.

E

817. Magnetite. Body of irregular form in paraschists of Shetland Metamorphic Series. South shoulder of Clothister Hill, $\frac{3}{4}$ mile W. of Sullom, Northmaven, Shetland. 1-in. 128 Scot., 6-in. 24 S.E. (965. Anal., B. E. Dixon). S 30030. Irregularly banded and intergrown with epidote and hornblende. *S.P.* 1934, Pt. I (1935), p. 83.

818. Magnetite, chromian. From talc-breunnerite-magnetite-rock; alteration of Corrycharmaig intrusive mass in schists of Dalradian Series. 470 yd S. 44° W. of sheepfold on path west from Corrycharmaig, Glen Lochay, Perthshire. 1-in. 46 Scot., 6-in. 67 S.E. (1495. Anal., C. O. Harvey; spect. det., J. A. C. McClelland). S 36767C. Magnetic fraction from rock in which the magnetite forms scattered crystals and granules in talc and breunnerite. Polished sections and X-ray powder examination suggest that chromite is not present in substantial amount. *Geol. Surv. Wartime Pamphlet* No. 9, ' Talc ', Supplement No. 1, 1949, p. 7. See also Nos. **726, 733-4, 819, 840.**

819. Breunnerite. From talc-breunnerite-magnetite-rock; alteration of Corrycharmaig intrusive mass in schists of Dalradian Series. 470 yd S. 44° W. of sheepfold on path west from Corrycharmaig, Glen Lochay, Perthshire. 1-in. 46 Scot., 6-in. 67 S.E. (1494. Anal., C. O. Harvey). S 36767B. Gravity separation of rock in which breunnerite forms coarse granular interlocking crystals containing abundant antigorite flakes, and is intergrown with talc. Chromian magnetite occurs in both talc and breunnerite. Sp. gr. $>2\cdot885$. The breunnerite shows a range of R.I. $\omega=1\cdot709-1\cdot716$. *Geol. Surv. Wartime Pamphlet* No. 9, ' Talc ', Supplement No. 1, 1949, p. 8. See also Nos. **726, 733-4, 818, 840.**

820. Siderite. From oolite chamositic siderite-rock of Main Oolitic Ironstone Group of Northampton Sand (Jurassic). Thingdon Mine, $1\frac{3}{8}$ miles S. 43° E. of Finedon Church, Northamptonshire. 1-in. 186, 6-in. 39 N.E. (1412. Anal., C. O. Harvey). E 20689. Sp. gr. (powder dried at 105°C)$=3\cdot62$. The R.I. shows a range $\omega=1\cdot775-1\cdot838$, with average value for large part of material $\omega=1\cdot816$. *M.G.S.* ' Petrology of the Northampton Sand Ironstone ', 1949, p. 48.

821. Siderite. From sphaerosiderite-rock produced by alteration of chamosite-mudstone of Northampton Sand Ironstone (Jurassic). $\frac{1}{2}$ mile W. 25° S. of West Field Lodge, $1\frac{1}{4}$ miles W.S.W. of Irthlingborough Church, Northamptonshire. 1-in. 186, 6-in. 39 N.E. (1411. Anal., C. O. Harvey). E 20688. Sp. gr. (powder dried at 105° C)$=3\cdot60$. R.I. shows a range $\omega=1\cdot760-1\cdot845$, with average value for large part of material $\omega=1\cdot813$. *M.G.S.* ' Petrology of the Northampton Sand Ironstone ', 1949, p. 48, pl. vi, fig. 6.

822. Siderite. From siderite-siltstone of Upper Siderite Mudstone—Limestone Group. 3-in. lenticle, 3 ft from top of Northampton Sand Ironstone (Jurassic). Stanion Lane Pit, $\frac{1}{4}$ mile N.E. of Stanion Lodge, near Corby, Northamptonshire. 1-in. 171, 6-in. 17 N.E. (1413. Anal., C. O. Harvey). E 20690. Sp. gr. (powder dried at 105°C)$=3\cdot58$. The R.I. shows a range $\omega=1\cdot789-1\cdot837$, with average value for large part of material $\omega=1\cdot812$. *M.G.S.* ' Petrology of the Northampton Sand Ironstone ', 1949, p. 48.

823. Stichtite, impure. Associated with chromite in serpentine. 665 yd E. 14° S. of trigonometrical height 800 on top of Hoo Field, Cunningsburgh, Dunrossness, Shetland. 1-in. 126 Scot., 6-in. 59 S.E. (931. Anal., B. E. Dixon). Sp. gr. (17°C)$=2\cdot19$. Rose-pink fibres showing no pleochroism. Straight extinction, positive elongation; R.I. for sodium light: $\alpha=1\cdot543$ or probably slightly lower, $\gamma=1\cdot559$. *S.P.* 1932, Pt. I (1933), p. 96. *Min. Mag.*, vol. xxiii, 1933, p. 313.

	820	821	822	. 823
SiO_2..	1·5	0·9	1·2	8·51
Al_2O_3	2·6	1·3	1·6	1·10
Fe_2O_3	1·5	0·4	0·6	6·52
FeO	47·92	46·89	45·83	8·95
MgO	2·46	3·37	3·68	26·72
CaO	3·71	4·66	5·10	0·10
$H_2O > 105°C$	2·4*	2·0*	2·1*	17·46
$H_2O < 105°C$	0·43	0·25	0·33	0·24
MnO	0·18	0·13	0·18	0·05
CO_2	33·33	35·36	35·20	3·14
Cr_2O_3	—	—	—	27·10
CdO	0·3	tr.	tr.	—
Insoluble residues	3·06	4·57	3 74	—
TOTAL	99·4	99·8	99·6	99·89

* Plus organic matter; calculated from loss on ignition.

824. Diopside. From Tireè Marble in Lewisian Gneiss. Shore section, N.E. end, Balephetrish, Tiree, Argyllshire. 1-in. 42 Scot., 6-in. 64 N.E. (1037. Anal., C. O. Harvey).
S 32453. Hypidiomorphic to rounded crystals in coarsely granular calcite. Numerous twin lamellae parallel to *a*. Sp. gr. $20°/20° = 3·29$. Pistachio-green in hand specimen, colourless in thin section. Optically$+$; axial plane (010); $Z : c = 38°$; $2V = 57°$; dispersion r>v; R.I. for sodium light: $\alpha = 1·673$, $\beta = 1·679$, $\gamma = 1·699$.
S.P. 1938 (1940), p. 94. *Min. Mag.*, vol. xxviii, 1947, p. 235; pl. xiv, figs. 1 and 2.

825. Fassaite. From inclusion in Tiree Marble in Lewisian Gneiss. Pink Marble Quarry, Balephetrish, Tiree, Argyllshire. 1-in. 42 Scot., 6-in. 64 N.E. (1038. Anal., C. O. Harvey).
S 32451. In aggregates with other silicates in pink calcite. Sp. gr. $20°/20° = 3·33$. Green in hand specimen, very pale green in thin section; optically $+$; axial plane (010); $Z : c = 45°$; $2V = 62°$; dispersionr $> v$; R.I. for sodium light: $\alpha = 1·688$, $\beta = 1·694$, $\gamma = 1·711$.
S.P. 1938 (1940), p. 94. *Min. Mag.*, vol. xxviii, 1947, p. 235; pl. xiv, figs. 4 and 5. See also Nos. **829, 833.**

826. Titanaugite. From patch or segregation in xenolith in the Haddo norite. Near Schivas, $4\frac{1}{2}$ miles N.W. of Ellon, Aberdeenshire. 1-in. 87 Scot. (P.1. Anal., B. E. Dixon).
Rounded crystals in a sphene-rich, plagioclase-diopside-hornfels xenolith. Well-developed cleavages parallel to (110) and (1Ī0), cleavage angle approximately 87°. Sp. gr. $= 3·43$. Black with slight purplish tinge. Pleochroism: $\alpha = \beta$ plum-coloured, γ light-yellow; absorption $\alpha = \beta > \gamma$; optically $+$, almost uniaxial; $Z : c = 32°$; intense dispersion; R.I. for sodium light: $\alpha = \beta = 1·741$, $\gamma = 1·762$.
S.P. 1933, Pt. I (1934), p. 91. *Zeits. Krist.*, vol. lxxxvi, 1933, p. 114. *Geol. Mag.*, vol. lxxv, 1938, p. 84.

827. Anthophyllite. In serpentine in Lewisian. Old quarry, 500 yd S. by E. of Borve Lodge and a few yards N.E. of Allt Sta, Sound of Taransay, South Harris, Inverness-shire. 1-in. 98 Scot., 6-in. Hebrides 17 N.E. (1515. Anal., W. F. Waters; spect. det., J. A. C. McClelland).
S 36762. Sp. gr. (air-dried powder)$= 3·01$. Straight extinction, slow elongation; R.I. for sodium light: $\gamma = 1·632$.

E*

	824	825	826	827	828
SiO_2 ..	54·23	51·04	37·52	58·48	53·16
Al_2O_3 ..	1·84	4·74	14·29	0·57	2·95
Fe_2O_3 ..	0·92	1·85	4·43	0·58	4·53
FeO	1·98	2·79	7·12	7·85	3·07
MgO ..	16·02	14·77	6·72	29·25	30·03
CaO ..	24·02	23·64	24·06	0·14	0·28
Na_2O ..	0·88	0·46	0·09	0·08	0·10
K_2O ..	0·03	0·15	tr.	0·02	0·01
$H_2O > 105°C$	0·04	0·16	n.d.	2·60	4·83
$H_2O < 105°C$	0·05	0·09	n.d.	0·20	0·41
TiO_2 ..	0·14	0·39	5·72	0·03	n.d.
P_2O_5 ..	tr.	tr.	—	tr.	0·01
MnO ..	0·23	0·17	0·14	0·27	0·14
CO_2.. ..	—	—	—	0·08	—
SO_3	—	—	—	n.d.	—
Cl	tr.	tr.	—	n.d.	—
F	tr.	tr.	—	n.d.	0·003
S	—	—	—	n.d.	0·18
Cr_2O_3 ..	—	—	0·11	0·04	0·52
V_2O_3 ..	—	—	—	n.d.(s)	—
NiO	—	—	—	0·01(s)	0·12
BaO ..	—	—	—	tr.(s)	tr.
SrO	—	—	—	tr.(s)	—
Li_2O ..	0·02	tr.		n.d.	—
TOTAL	100·40	100·25	100·20	100·20	100·34
Less O for S	—	—	—	—	0·07
	100·40	100·25	100·20	100·20	100·27

828. Anthophyllite. Lenses in serpentinized peridotite in Lewisian. Scara Ruadh, 500 yd E. of the S.E. end of Loch Langavat, South Harris, Inverness-shire. 1-in. 89 Scot., 6-in. Hebrides 23 N.W. (1516. Anal., W. F. Waters and K. L. H. Murray).
S 36764. Straight extinction, slow elongation; R.I. for sodium light: $\alpha = 1·596$, $\gamma = 1·625$.

829. Pargasite. From inclusion in Tiree Marble in Lewisian Gneiss. Pink Marble Quarry, Balephetrish, Tiree, Argyllshire. 1-in. 42 Scot., 6-in. 64 N.E. (1039. Anal., C. O. Harvey).
S 32451. In aggregates with other silicates in pink calcite. Sp. gr. 20°/20° = 3·175. Pleochroism: α yellow, β yellow-green, γ bluish-green; axial plane (010); Z: c = 22°; 2V = 86°; dispersion slight; R.I. for sodium light: $\alpha = 1·659$, $\beta = 1·668$, $\gamma = 1·677$.
S.P. 1938 (1940), p. 94. *Amer. Min.*, vol. xxviii, 1943, p. 85. *Min. Mag.*, vol. xxviii, 1947, p. 235; pl. xiv, figs. 3, 5 and 6.
See also Nos. **825, 833.**

830. Riebeckite. From granophyric riebeckite-felsite, ? Old Red Sandstone. E. end of Beorgs of Uyea, 280 yd S.S.W. of S.E. corner of Pettadale Water, North Roe, Shetland. 1-in. 130 Scot., 6-in. 14 N.E. (1575. Anal., C. O. Harvey; spect. det., J. A. C. McClelland. Semi-micro. analysis).
S 35303. Sp. gr. (21°C, of powder dried at 105°C) = 3·32. Pleochroism: α indigo-blue, β brownish-yellow, γ indigo-blue. Optically—; axial plane normal to (010); X: c = 3°-4°; 2V = about 80°; R.I. for sodium light: $\alpha = 1·701$, $\beta = 1·710$, $\gamma = 1·717$.
Min. Mag., vol. xxix, 1950, p. 368.

831. Garnet. From Ben Lui Garnetiferous Mica-Schists of·Dalradian Series. Shira-Clachan hydroelectric tunnel, S.E. drive from Brannie Burn, 1715 yd from chainage zero point in Brannie Burn, near head of Loch Fyne, Argyllshire. 1-in. 37 Scot., 6-in. 126 S.W. (1648. Anal., A. D. Wilson; spect. det., C. O. Harvey).
S 40378. Cell-size $a=11 \cdot 59_5$Å. R.I. for sodium light: n=1·798. The analysis may be interpreted as:—almandine, 70·7; grossular, 17·6; pyrope, 4·8; andradite, 2·0; spessartine, 1·5; remainder, 3·7.
S.P. 1954 (1955), p. 61.

	829	830	831	832	833
SiO_2 ..	41·72	51·3	37·6	47·74	39·1
Al_2O_3 ..	15·86	2·7	21·8	34·19	17·6
Fe_2O_3 ..	3·36	14·2	0·7	0·95	1·1
FeO.. ..	6·03	18·5	30·7	0·22	6·8
MgO ..	14·14	n.d.	1·4	0·63	18·7
CaO ..	12·92	1·1	7·2	0·04	1·2
Na_2O ..	1·42	6·0	—	0·34	0·5
K_2O ..	2·60	1·4	—	11·27	9·5
$H_2O > 105°C$	0·85	1·9	—	4·37	—
$H_2O < 105°C$	0·04	0·1	—	0·18	—
TiO_2 ..	0·81	1·9	0·3	0·11	1·9
P_2O_5 ..	tr.	n.d.	—	0·04	tr.
MnO ..	0·12	0·9	0·6	0·04	0·1
B_2O_3 ..	—	—	—	0·2(s)	—
Cl	0·46	—	—	—	0·3
F	0·16	0·3	—	0·24	0·2
S·	—	—	—	0·01	—
Cr_2O_3 ..	—	n.d.	—	n.d.	—
V_2O_3 ..	—	n.d.(s)	—	—	—
NiO.. ..	—	n.d.(s)	—	—	—
BaO.. ..	—	—	—	0·05	0·5
Li_2O ..	0·02	tr.(s)	—	n.d.	tr.
TOTAL	100·51	100·3	100·3*	100·62	—
Less O for Cl, F	0·18	0·1	—	0·10	—
	100·33	100·2	100·3	100·52	—

* Approximate spect. det.:—Cr: 0·003. Sc: 0·005. V:0·004. Yt: 0·01.

832. Muscovite. From hydrothermal wolfram vein. Harding Vein Level, Carrock Wolfram Mine, Mosedale, Cumberland. 1-in. 23, 6-in. 47 S.E. (1561. Anal., W. F. Waters, K. L. H. Murray and Miss A. Shollick; spect. det., J. A. C. McClelland).
E 23652. Coarse-grained yellow muscovite. R.I.: $\gamma=1·593$.

833. Biotite. From inclusion in Tiree Marble in Lewisian Gneiss. Pink Marble Quarry, Balephetrish, Tiree, Argyllshire. 1-in. 42 Scot., 6-in. 64 N.E. (1040. Anal., C. O. Harvey. Semi-micro. analysis).
S 32451. In aggregates with other silicates in pink calcite. Sp. gr. 20°/20°=2·89. Pleochroism: ω brown, ε pale straw coloured; optically −, practically uniaxial; R.I. for sodium light: ω=1·618, ε=1·573.
S.P. 1938 (1940), p. 94. *Min. Mag.*, vol. xxviii, 1947, p. 235; pl. xiv, fig. 6. See also Nos. **825, 829.**

834. Chloritoid. From chloritoid-schist, Shetland Metamorphic Series. Top of cliff, 465 yd N.E. of Ness of Snabrough, 235 yd S.W. by W. of Dale of·Oddsta, Fetlar, Shetland. 1-in. 130 Scot., 6-in. 12 S.W. (1649. Anal., A. D. Wilson and P. Coombs; spect. det., C. O. Harvey and K. L. H. Murray).

S 40131. Pleochroism: α grey-green, β indigo-blue, γ pale golden-yellow; absorption: β>α>γ; optically +; 2V=68°; dispersion strong, r>v. R.I. for sodium light: α=1·721, β=1·723–1·724, γ=1·729.
S.P. 1954 (1955), p. 61.

835. Daphnite. From vein in chloritic killas (metamorphosed slate of ? Devonian age). In New Tolgus Shaft, 1400–1500 ft deep, Tolgus Mine, near Redruth, Cornwall. 1-in. 352, 6-in. 63 N.E. (1020. Anal., C. O. Harvey).
E 13984, M I 16006. Cell dimensions: $a=5·40$Å, $b=9·36$Å, c' (spacing, not the cell dimension c)=28·2Å. Fan-like aggregates of soft flexible laminae. Sp. gr. =3·08. Dark-green. Pleochroism: ω green, ε pale greenish-yellow; optically—; R.I. for sodium light: ω=1·655, ε=1·646.
Min. Mag., vol. xxv, 1939, p. 443; pl. xviii, fig. 1; pl. xix, fig. 13.

836. Chamosite. Green chloritic content in shell in ironstone bed of Frodingham Ironstone (Lower Lias, Jurassic). Ironstone quarries, Frodingham, Lincoln-shire. 1-in. 80/89. (1015. Anal., C. O. Harvey. Semi-micro. analysis).
E 17573, M I 26729. Distinct granules, each composed of a felted mass of minute green flakes. Sp. gr.=3·242. R.I. for sodium light: approximately 1·665.
Min. Mag., vol. xxv, 1939, p. 445; pl. xviii, figs. 2-4; pl. xix, fig. 1. *Min. Mag.*, vol. xxvii, 1945, pp. 102, 106; pl. viii, fig. 2. *M.G.S.* ' Liassic Ironstones ', 1952, p. 18.

	834	835	836	837	838	839
SiO_2 ..	24·0	24·35	19·77	27·8	34·1	32·5
Al_2O_3 ..	40·0	20·21	12·40	17·4	16·9	16·9
Fe_2O_3 ..	1·8	2·13	5·74	15·4	14·2	4·1
FeO ..	23·3	36·27	31·02	18·5	14·8	24·4
MgO ..	2·6	5·57	3·63	1·8	2·0	2·8
CaO ..	0·1	0·10	3·34	0·3	0·4	2·0
Na_2O ..	—	—	—	—	—	0·1
K_2O ..	—	—	—	—	—	0·1
$H_2O>105°C$	7·0	10·46	—	12·1†	11·5†	9·2
$H_2O<105°C$	n.d.	0·35	—	4·3	4·2	3·0
TiO_2 ..	1·0	0·04	—	0·7	0·6	1·9
P_2O_5 ..	—	—	0·26	0·5	0·5	tr.
MnO ..	0·3	0·48	0·35	n.d.-tr.	n.d.-tr.	tr.
				(s)	(s)	
CO_2 ..	—	—	4·22	—	—	2·9
SO_3	—	—	0·32	—	—	n.d.
S	—	—	—	—	—	0·1
FeS_2 ..	—	—	—	0·6‡	0·3 ‡	—
Cr_2O_3 ..	—	—	—	0·1	0·1	tr.
V_2O_3 ..	—	—	—	0·3	0·2	—
BaO ..	—	—	—	—	—	n.d.
SrO	—	—	—	—	—	tr.(s)
PbO ..	—	—	—	—	—	tr.(s)
ZnO ..	—	—	—	—	—	0·1(s)
Li_2O ..	—	—	—	—	—	tr.
Insoluble residue ..	—	—	7·8	—	—	—
Rarer oxides	0·1(s)*	—	—	—	—	—
TOTAL	100·2	99·96	—	99·8	99·8	100·1

* Approximate percentages:—ZrO_2: 0·03. Cr_2O_3: 0·02. V_2O_3: 0·03. NiO: 0·01. CoO: 0·01. BaO: 0·002. SrO: 0·002. Ga_2O_3: 0·01. Sc_2O_3: 0·004.
† Calculated from loss on ignition.
‡ Total S calculated as FeS_2.

837. Chamosite. From chamositic oolite of Northampton Sand Ironstone (Jurassic), 4 ft above base of workable ironstone. Irthlingborough Mine, 1070 yd W. 1° S. of Irthlingborough Church, Northamptonshire. 1-in. 186, 6-in. 40 N.W. (1426. Anal., C. O. Harvey; spect. det., J. A. C. McClelland). E 20785. Light- to dark-green chamosite. Range of R.I.: 1·630–1·668, approximate average value 1·652. *M.G.S.* ' Petrology of the Northampton Sand Ironstone ', 1949, p. 43.

838. Chamosite. From sandy chamositic oolite of Northampton Sand Ironstone (Jurassic), 6 ft above floor of seam. Irthlingborough Mine, 1220 yd W. 20° S of Irthlingborough Church, Northamptonshire. 1-in. 186, 6-in. 39 N.E. (1427. Anal., C. O. Harvey; spect. det., J. A. C. McClelland). E 20786. Light- to dark-green chamosite. Range of R.I.: 1·621–1·653, approximate average value 1·640. *M.G.S.* ' Petrology of the Northampton Sand Ironstone ', 1949, p. 43.

839. Chamosite. Ooliths from chamosite-oolite forming lower part of Cleveland Mine Ironstone Seam (Jurassic). Straight West Working, Longacres Mine, Skelton, North Riding, Yorkshire. 1-in. 34, 6-in. 18 N.W. (1482. Anal., C. O. Harvey; spect. det., J. A. C. McClelland. Semi-micro. analysis). E 21592B. Heavy concentrate (sp. gr. >2·64) from ooliths insoluble in cold dilute hydrochloric acid. Some quartz and siderite are present. *M.G.S.* ' Liassic Ironstones ', 1952, p. 25; pl. ii, fig. 5. See also No. **815.**

840. Talc. From talc-breunnerite-magnetite-rock; alteration of Corrycharmaig intrusive mass in schists of Dalradian Series. 470 yd S. 44° W. of sheepfold on path west from Corrycharmaig, Glen Lochay, Perthshire. 1-in. 46 Scot., 6-in. 67 S.E. (1493. Anal., C. O. Harvey). S 36767 A. Light fraction from gravity separation: talc with some antigorite. In the rock the talc forms aggregates containing antigorite flakes and is intergrown with coarser granular breunnerite; chromian magnetite grains occur mainly in the talc and partly in the breunnerite. Sp. gr <2·885. *Geol. Surv. Wartime Pamphlet* No. 9, ' Talc ', Supplement No. 1, 1949, p. 8. See also Nos. **726, 733-4, 818-9.**

841. Glauconite. From glauconite sand, middle division of Bracklesham Beds (Eocene). Trenches on Oystershell Hill, N. slopes of Staple Hill, Chobham Common, Surrey. 1-in. 269, 6-in. 10 S.E. (1324. Anal., C. O. Harvey; spect. det., J. A. C. McClelland). British Museum (Natural History) specimen 1926, 526. *Geol. Surv. Wartime Pamphlet* No. 33, ' Glauconite Sand ', 1943, p. 3. *Amer. Min.*, vol. xxviii, 1943, p. 542.

842. Kaolinite. Thin bed 10 ft above Seven Feet Coal, in red Middle Coal Measures (Carboniferous). 3350 yd W. of Mancetter Church, 1300 yd N.E. of Bentley Church, Warwickshire. 1-in. 169, 6-in. 6 S.W. (1572. Anal., W. F. Waters and K. L. H. Murray; spect. det., J. A. C. McClelland). E 23933. Massive greenish-white hard clay of extremely fine grain size; shown by X-ray powder examination to be kaolinite. R.I. approximately 1·565, apparently nearly isotropic. There are a few narrow chlorite veinlets and a little iron-staining.

843. Dickite. Associated with collophane (No. **878**) coating joints in Magnesian Limestone (Permian). 246-250 ft deep, Hesleden Dene Water Borehole No. 2, 1¾ miles E.S.E. of Castle Eden, Co. Durham. 1-in. 27, 6-in. 29 S.W. (1472. Anal., C. O. Harvey. Semi-micro. analysis). E 21576. Colourless hexagonal flakes. Optically probably +; axial angle large; R.I. for sodium light: α=1·560, γ=1·566. *Min. Mag.*, vol. xxviii, 1948, p. 339; pl. xx. figs. 1 and 2.

	840	841	842	843	844	845
SiO_2 ..	58·10	50·40	44·16	45·4	2·10	0·5
Al_2O_3 ..	0·54	6·46	36·24	39·2	tr.	⎫
Fe_2O_3 ..	0·47	20·17	0·92	0·2*	tr.	⎬ 2·3(s)
FeO ..	2·44	1·43	0·10	—	—	⎭
MgO ..	31·28	4·34	0·44	0·3	—	31·0
CaO ..	0·26	0·03(s)	0·32	tr.	6·30	0·2(s)
Na_2O ..	—	0·11	0·19	tr.	—	—
K_2O ..	—	7·57	0·55	0·2	—	—
$H_2O > 105°C$	6·23	5·02	12·63	13·4	0·06	—
$H_2O < 105°C$	0·17	4·06	3·46	0·4	—	—
TiO_2 ..	0·03	0·09	1·15	n.d.	—	—
P_2O_5 ..	n.d.	0·04	0·05	n.d.	26·80	—
MnO ..	0·01	0·02	tr.	n.d.	—	tr.(s)
CO_2 ..	0·17	n.d.	0·01	tr.	—	—
B_2O_3 ..	—	—	—	—	—	60·
Cl	—	—	—	—	—	8·6
F	—	<0·02	0·02	—	—	—
S	—	0·03	0·03	—	—	—
Cr_2O_3 ..	0·18	0·03	0·03	—	—	—
V_2O_3 ..	—	—	tr.(s)	—	—	—
NiO ..	0·19	—	tr.(s)	—	—	—
BaO ..	n.d.	n.d.(s)	tr.(s)	—	—	—
SrO	—	—	tr.(s)	—	—	—
PbO ..	—	—	—	—	0·92	—
Li_2O ..	—	tr.	0·17	—	—	—
Rb_2O ..	—	0·02(s)	—	—	—	—
Cs_2O ..	—	n.d.(s)	—	—	—	—
ThO_2 ..	—	—	—	—	31·50	—
U_3O_8 ..	—	—	—	—	4·05	—
Ce_2O_3 ..	—	—	—	—	14·21	—
$(La,\&c)_2O_3$	—	—	—	—	13·35‡	—
Carbonaceous matter ..	—	—	—	1·0†	—	—
TOTAL	100·07	99·82	100·47	100·1	99·29	102·6
Less O for S,Cl,F ..	—	—	0·02	—	—	2·0
	100·07	99·82	100·45	100·1	99·29	100·6

* Fe calculated as Fe_2O_3.
† Loss on ignition other than H_2O.
‡ Major constituents: La, Pr, Nd; minor constituents: Gd, Sm, Yt.

844. Cheralite. From kaolinized pegmatite dyke. Kuttakuzhi, Kalkulum taluk, 23 miles E.S.E. of Trivandrum, Travancore, India. (Anal., Radiochemical Division, Chemical Research Laboratory).
Approximate cell dimensions: $a = 6·74$Å; $b = 7·00$Å, $c = 6·43$Å, $\beta = 104·6°$. Cleavages: (010) distinct, (100) difficult, parting on (001) poor. Uneven fracture; hardness = 5. Sp. gr. (determined by pyknometer using carbon tetrachloride) = $5·3 \pm 0·1$. Resinous to vitreous lustre; pale- to dark-green, pale-green in thin section; white streak. Pleochroism faint: $\alpha = \beta$ green, γ green with yellow tinge; optically +; $\alpha = b$, $\gamma : c = 7°$; $2V = 17·4° - 19·0°$, mean value 18·1°, calculated value 17·9°; dispersion of optic axes not perceptible: R.I.: $\alpha = 1·779$, $\beta = 1·780$, $\gamma = 1·816$.
Min. Mag., vol. xxx, 1953, p. 95.

845. Boracite. From Permian Middle Evaporite Bed. 4090–4160 ft deep, Eskdale No. 2 Borehole, near Aislaby, Eskdale, Yorkshire. 1-in. 43, 6-in. 32 S.W. (1316. Anal., C. O. Harvey; spect. det., J. A. C. McClelland. Semi-micro. analysis). E 19994. Hardness about equal to that of quartz. Sp. gr.=2·95. Dull vitreous lustre; colourless to greyish-white translucent corroded crystals. Optically +; 2V=82½°; R.I. for sodium light: α=1·658, β=1·662, γ=1·668.
The Analyst, vol. lxviii, 1943, p. 212. *Min. Mag.*, vol. xxvii, 1944, p. 51.

VI. PARTIAL ANALYSES OF MINERALS

846. Galena. Vein or replacement in Carboniferous Limestone. Old lead mine in Leigh Woods (near Bristol), E. of Abbots Leigh, Somerset. 1-in. 264, 6-in. 3 S.W. (1585. Anal., W. F. Waters; spect. det., Department of the Government Chemist).
Pb: 84·1%. Ag: tr. (<0·01; s). Bi: n.d. (s). As: <0·01(s). Sb: n.d.(s). Tl: n.d.(s).

847. Galena. Tips from old lead mines formerly working galena-baryte veins cutting Carboniferous Limestone. Bourton Combe, 700 yd W. of church at Barrow Court and 1000 yd S. of Flax Bourton Church, Somerset. 1-in. 264, 6 in. 5 S.E. (1594. Anal., C. O. Harvey). M I 28288.
Pb: 82·7%. Ag: <0·01%. Bi: n.d. As: n.d. Sb: tr. Tl: n.d.

848. Galena. Vein cutting Carboniferous Limestone. Corporation Quarry, Upper Knole, Brentry, Bristol, Gloucestershire. 1-in. 264, 6-in. 71 N.E. (1593. Anal., C. O. Harvey). E 24523.
Pb: 82·7%. Ag: <0·01%. Bi: tr. As: n.d. Sb: tr. Tl: n.d.

849. Galena. Vein cutting Carboniferous Limestone. Quarry, Wick, 1600 yd S.W. of Doynton Church and 1050 yd S. of Gatherham Farm, Abson, Gloucestershire. 1-in. 265, 6-in. 73 S.W. (1595. Anal., C. O. Harvey). M I 28289.
Pb: 81·2%. Ag: 0·02%. Bi: tr. As: n.d. Sb: about 0·1%. Tl: n.d.

850. Sphalerite. Hand-picked sample from dump at mine. Stonecroft Lead Mine, 2¼ miles W.N.W. of Fourstones, Northumberland. 1-in. 13, 6-in. 81 S.E. New Series. (1422. Spect. det., J. A. C. McClelland).
Pale-brown sphalerite.
M.G.S. ' N. Pennine Orefield ', vol. i, 1948, p. 88.
Approximate figures (s):—Cd: 0·25%. Cu: 0·02%. Ag: tr.–0·01%. Sb: n.d.

851. Sphalerite. Hand-picked sphalerite from dumps. Minera Lead-Zinc Mines, 4 miles W. of Wrexham, Denbighshire. 1-in. 121, 6-in. 28 N.W. (1550. Anal., C. O. Harvey; spect. det., J. A. C. McClelland).
Fe: 0·20%. Cd: 1±0·5%(s). Ge: 0·02%(s).

852. Sphalerite concentrate. From flotation treatment of dumps from jig-dressing. Nenthead Lead-Zinc Mines, Alston, Cumberland. 1-in. 25, 6-in. 42 N.E. (1418. Anal., C. O. Harvey; spect. det., J. A. C. McClelland).
M.G.S. ' N. Pennine Orefield ', vol. i, 1948, p. 88.
Zn: 59·9%. Pb: 2·02%. Mn: 0·02%. Fe: 3·2%. Total S: 31·9%. Insoluble matter: 1·42%. Approximate figures (s):—Cd: 0·26%. Cu: 0·1%. Ag: tr.–0·01%. Sb: tr.–0·05%. Mg: 0·1%. Si: 0·4%. Ca: 0·2–0·3%. Mo: 0·02–0·05%. Sn: tr.
The concentrate also contained small percentages of sulphate, carbonate, moisture and organic matter.

853. Fluorite. From crystal in cavity in metasomatic flats in limestone of Carboniferous Limestone Series. Boltsburn East Mine, Rookhope, Co. Durham. 1-in. 25, 6-in. 23 N.E. (1419. Spect. det., J. A. C. McClelland).
Purple cleavage fragments showing brilliant bluish fluorescence.
M.G.S. ' N. Pennine Orefield ', vol. i, 1948, p. 90. *Min. Res.*, vol. iv, ' Fluorspar ', 4th edit., 1952, p. 10.
See table, p. 69.
Other trace elements:—Be: n.d. Sr: tr. Yb: present. La: tr.

854. Fluorite. Gravity concentrate from veins in Carboniferous Limestone Series. Stotfield Burn Mine, Rookhope, Co. Durham. 1-in. 25, 6-in. 23 N.E. (1497. Spect. det., J. A. C. McClelland).
Greyish coarse powder showing brilliant blue fluorescence.
Min. Res., vol. iv, ' Fluorspar ', 4th edit., 1952, p. 10.
See table, p. 69.
Other trace elements:—Be: n.d. Sr: tr. Yb: present. La: present.

855. Fluorite. Gravity concentrate from vein in Carboniferous Limestone Series. Sedling Mine, Wearhead, Co. Durham. 1-in. 25, 6-in. 22 N.E. (1498. Spect. det., J. A. C. McClelland).
Greyish coarse powder. Brilliant blue fluorescence shown by most grains.
Min. Res., vol. iv, ' Fluorspar ', 4th edit., 1952, p. 10.
See table below.
Other trace elements:—Be: n.d. Sr: tr. Yb: present. La: present.

856. Fluorite. Flotation concentrate from deposits in Carboniferous Limestone Series. Glebe Mine, Eyam, Derbyshire. 1-in. 99, 6-in. 16 N.E. (1499. Spect. det., J. A. C. McClelland).
White fine-grained powder. Little, if any, fluorescence.
Min. Res., vol. iv, ' Fluorspar ', 4th edit., 1952, p. 10.
See table below.
Other trace elements:—Be: n.d. Sr: tr. Yb: n.d. La: n.d.

Percentage of element

	Yt	Eu	Ce	Th	U
853	0·03	0·005	n.d. <0·001	n.d. <0·01	n.d. <0·02
854	0·06	0·007	0·01–0·02	n.d. <0·01	0·02?*
855	0·04	0·005	0·01	n.d. <0·01	n.d. <0·01
856	0·005	n.d. <0·001	n.d. <0·001	n.d. <0·01	n.d. <0·02
857	0·02	n.d. <0·001	n.d. <0·001	n.d. <0·01	n.d. <0·01
858	0·08	0·007	n.d. <0·01	n.d. <0·05	n.d. <0·05
859	0·12	0·010	n.d. 0·01	n.d. <0·05	n.d. <0·05
860	0·11	0·011	n.d. <0·01	n.d. <0·05	0·01–0·1?*
861	0·02	n.d. <0·001	n.d. <0·001	n.d. <0·01	n.d. <0·01
862	0·05	0·003	n.d. <0·001	n.d. <0·01	n.d. <0·01
863	0·04	0·002	n.d. <0·001	n.d. <0·01	n.d. <0·01

* Doubtful.

857. Fluorite. White crystal from vein in Carboniferous Limestone Series. Greenhow Rake, Greenhow, 3 miles W. of Pateley Bridge, Yorkshire. 1-in. 61, 6-in. 135. (1500. Spect. det., J. A. C. McClelland).
No visible fluorescence.
Min. Res., vol. iv, ' Fluorspar ', 4th edit., 1952, p. 10.
See table above.
Other trace elements:—Be: n.d. Sr: tr. Yb: n.d. La: n.d.

858. Fluorite. Tailings from Rispey Mill, Rookhope, Co. Durham. 1-in. 25, 6-in 23 N.W. (1501. Spect. det., J. A. C. McClelland).
Dark-grey coarse powder. Bluish fluorescence shown by some grains.
Min. Res., vol. iv, ' Fluorspar ', 4th edit., 1952, p. 10.
See table, p. 69.
Other trace elements:—Be: n.d. Sr: tr. Yb: present. La: present.

859. Fluorite. Tailings from Sharnberry High Level dumps (from vein in Carboniferous Limestone Series). $6\frac{1}{2}$ miles W. of Hamsterley, and approximately 5 miles S. by E. of Stanhope, Co. Durham. 1-in. 26, 6-in. 32 S.W. (1502. Spect. det., J. A. C. McClelland).
Brown coarse powder. Bluish fluorescence shown by some grains.
Min. Res., vol. iv, ' Fluorspar ', 4th edit., 1952, p. 10.
See table, p. 69.
Other trace elements:—Be: n.d. Sr: tr. Yb: n.d. La: n.d.

860. Fluorite. Tailings from dumps (from deposits in Carboniferous Limestone Series). California mine dumps, 5 miles S. of Stanhope, Co. Durham. 1-in. 26, 6-in. 32 S.W. (1503. Spect. det., J. A. C. McClelland).
Coarse particles, some brown, some white. Brilliant bluish fluorescence by white particles only.
Min. Res., vol. iv, ' Fluorspar ', 4th edit., 1952, p. 10.
See table, p. 69.
Other trace elements:—Be: n.d. Sr: tr. Yb: n.d. La: n.d.

861. Fluorite. From replacement deposit in reef limestone of Carboniferous Limestone Series. Treak Cliff Mine, 1 mile W. of Castleton, Derbyshire. 1-in. 99, 6-in. 9 N.E. (1504. Spect. det., J. A. C. McClelland).
Purple crystal. No visible fluorescence.
Min. Res., vol. iv, ' Fluorspar ', 4th edit., 1952, p. 10.
See table, p. 69.
Other trace elements:—Be: n.d. Sr: present. Yb: n.d. La: n.d.

862. Fluorite. South side flats, Rotherhope Fell Mine, Alston Moor, Cumberland. 1-in. 25, 6-in. 41 N.E. (1505. Spect. det., J. A. C. McClelland).
White crystalline material. Brilliant bluish fluorescence.
Min. Res., vol. iv, ' Fluorspar ', 4th edit., 1952, p. 10.
See table, p. 69.
Other trace elements:—Be: n.d. Sr: tr. Yb: tr. La: n.d.

863. Fluorite. From replacement deposit in Carboniferous Limestone Series. Scordale Mines, $2\frac{1}{2}$ miles N.E. of Hilton, Westmorland. 1-in. 31, 6-in. 10 S.W. (1507. Spect. det., J. A. C. McClelland).
Amber crystal. Bluish fluorescence.
Min. Res., vol. iv, ' Fluorspar ', 4th edit., 1952, p. 10.
See table, p. 69.
Other trace elements:—Be: n.d. Sr: tr. Yb: tr. La: n.d.

864. Iron ore. Dumps from shaft on Ardale Head Vein near Little Limestone (Carboniferous Limestone Series) outcrop. Ardale Head Ironstone Mine, 3 miles E.N.E. of Ousby, Cumberland. 1-in. 24, 6-in. 51 N.E. (1171. Anal., G. A. Sergeant). E 18814, X-ray films Nos. 1135–I, 1135A–I, 1136.
Yellowish-brown cavernous goethite with a brown, sometimes fibrous, crust of goethite mixed with haematite. There is a little fine-grained quartz.
Geol. Surv. Wartime Pamphlet No. 14, ' Iron Ore Deposits of the N. Pennines ', 1941, p. 23. *M.G.S.* ' N. Pennine Orefield ', vol. i, 1948, p. 127.
SiO_2: 11·3%. Fe_2O_3: 65·7%. FeO: tr. $H_2O > 105°C$: 9·6%. $H_2O < 105°C$: 1·5%. P_2O_5: 1·1%. MnO: about 4%.

865. Iron Ore. Open cut in ore-body replacing Great Limestone (Carboniferous Limestone Series). Ardale Head Ironstone Mine, 3 miles E.N.E. of Ousby, Cumberland. 1-in. 24, 6-in. 51 N.E. (1172. Anal., G. A. Sergeant). E 18815, X-ray films Nos. 1035, 1041, 1051.

Goethite with numerous small quartz grains.
Geol. Surv. Wartime Pamphlet No. 14, ' Iron Ore Deposits of the N. Pennines ',
1941, p. 23. *M.G.S.* ' N. Pennine Orefield ', vol. i, 1948, p. 127.
SiO_2: 13·1%. Fe_2O_3: 65·7%. FeO: tr. $H_2O > 105°C$: 10·4%. $H_2O < 105°C$:
1·4%. P_2O_5: 0·9%. MnO: about 0·5%.

866. Iron ore. Southern part of Park Grove Sun Vein in Great Limestone (Carboniferous Limestone Series). Open cut and dumps in Blackhouse Plantation,
E. side of Park Fell, 1¼ miles S.W. of Alston Church, Cumberland. 1-in. 25,
6-in. 33 S.E. (1178. Anal., G. A. Sergeant). E 18839, X-ray films Nos. 1135–IV,
1135A–IV, 1160.
Reddish-yellow haematite mixed with goethite. There are abundant small
cavities. Quartz is present in very fine grains, mainly <0·01 mm.
Geol. Surv. Wartime Pamphlet No. 14, ' Iron Ore Deposits of the N. Pennines ',
1941, p. 26. *M.G.S.* ' N. Pennine Orefield ', vol. i, 1948, p. 145.
SiO_2: 24·6%. Fe_2O_3: 56·4%. FeO: tr. CaO: 0·2%. $H_2O < 105°C$: 1·4%.
P_2O_5: 0·1%. MnO: 0·9%. S: 0·2%.

867. Siderite. Donks Vein replacement of south wall in Great Limestone (Carboniferous Limestone Series). Boltsburn West Level Mine, Rookhope, Co. Durham.
1-in. 25, 6-in. 23 N.E. (1174. Anal., C. O. Harvey). E 18817.
R.I. ω=1·843.
Geol. Surv. Wartime Pamphlet No. 14, ' Iron Ore Deposits of the N. Pennines ',
1941, p. 7. *M.G.S.* ' N. Pennine Orefield ', vol. i, 1948, pp. 93, 230.
SiO_2: 2·7%. Fe_2O_3: 1·6%.* FeO: 47·1%.* $H_2O > 105°C$: 0·2%. H_2O
<105°C: 0·1%. P_2O_5: tr.
* Figures not accurate owing to probable presence of organic matter.

868. Witherite. Vein in Great Limestone (Carboniferous Limestone Series). Treloar
Vein stopes, E. of Liverick Vein, Nentsberry Mine (adit entrance, Nentsberry,
Alston, Cumberland), Northumberland. 1-in. 25, 6-in. 110 N.E. Old Series.
(1162. Anal., C. O. Harvey; spect. det., H. K. Whalley). E 18745.
Geol. Surv. Wartime Pamphlet No. 46, ' Barium Minerals ', 1945, p. 25. *M.G.S.*
' N. Pennine Orefield ', vol. i, 1948, pp. 95, 192.
SiO_2: 0·7%. CaO: 1%. $H_2O < 105°C$: n.d. Total S: 0·4%. BaO: 74%.
Sr: approximately 1·0% (s). Zn: approximately 0·04%(s).

869. Witherite. Vein in Coal Measures (Carboniferous). Morrison Pit, South Moor
Colliery, South Moor, Co. Durham. 1-in. 20/26, 6-in. 19 N.W. (1421. Spect.
det., J. A. C. McClelland).
Single crystal of pure witherite.
Geol. Surv. Wartime Pamphlet No. 46, ' Barium Minerals ', 1945, p. 4. *M.G.S.*
' N. Pennine Orefield ', vol. i, 1948, p. 95.
Approximate percentages (s):—Ca: 0·03. Sr: 0·35. Pb: 0·02–0·04.

870. Barytocalcite. Dump from main level at Great Limestone horizon (Carboniferous Limestone Series). Fistas Rake, Blagill Mine, Cumberland. 1-in. 25,
6-in. 34 N.W. (1163. Anal., C. O. Harvey; spect. det., H. K. Whalley). E 18746.
Optically −; 2V=15½°; R.I.: γ=1·688.
Geol. Surv. Wartime Pamphlet No. 46, ' Barium Minerals ', 1945, p. 4. *M.G.S.*
' N. Pennine Orefield ', vol. i, 1948, pp. 95, 147.
SiO_2: 0·7%. CaO: 19%. $H_2O < 105°C$: n.d. Total S: 0·3%. BaO: 50%.
Sr: approximately 0·3%(s). Zn: negligible (s).

871. Feldspar. From Ben Loyal post-Moine syenite mass. Quarry, 400 yd W. of
Loch Loyal Lodge, W. of Loch Loyal, approximately 7 miles S. of Tongue,
Sutherland. 1-in. 108 Scot., 6-in. 35 S.W. (1169. Anal., C. O. Harvey). S 34602.
' Non-magnetic ' portion separated magnetically by A. F. Hallimond from
alkali-syenite. Sp. gr.=2·59.

Geol. Surv. Wartime Pamphlet No. 2, Supplement No. 1, ' Electro-magnetic separation tests on Scottish Alkaline Syenites ', 1941, p. 3. *Geol. Surv. Wartime Pamphlet* No. 44, ' Scottish Sources of Alkali Feldspar ', 1945, p. 23.
Total Fe calculated as Fe_2O_3: 0·2%. Na_2O: 4·5%. K_2O: 9·6%. $H_2O < 105°C$: tr.

872. **Feldspar.** From Loch Ailsh post-Cambrian major intrusion. N.E. side of south peak of Sail an Ruathair, fully $1\frac{1}{2}$ miles N.N.E. of Benmore Lodge, Assynt, Sutherland. 1-in. 102 Scot., 6-in. 83 S.W. (1167–8. Anal., C. O. Harvey). S 34601.
Portions separated magnetically by A. F. Hallimond from perthosite, Analysis 116, *M.G.S.* ' Chemical Analyses ', 1931.
Geol. Surv. Wartime Pamphlet No. 2, Supplement No. 1, ' Electro-magnetic separation tests on Scottish Alkaline Syenites ', 1941, p. 3.
1167. Separated in field of strength sufficient to remove monazite. Sp. gr.$=2·61$.
Total Fe calculated as Fe_2O_3: 0·7%. Na_2O: 7·6%. K_2O: 5·6%. $H_2O < 105°C$: tr.
1168. ' Non-magnetic ' portion. Sp. gr.$=2·63$.
Total Fe calculated as Fe_2O_3: 0·6%. Na_2O: 8·0%. K_2O: 5·1%. $H_2O < 105°C$: tr.

873. **Aegirine.** From post-Cambrian aegirine-nepheline-syenite-pegmatite dyke. Bad na h'Achlaise, 700 yd S. of Ledmore, Assynt, Sutherland. 1-in. 101 Scot., 6-in. 91 N.E. (1562. Anal., Miss A. Shollick; spect. det., J. A. C. McClelland). S 37399.
Pleochroism: $\alpha=\beta$ deep-green, γ yellowish-brown;   absorption $\alpha>\beta=\gamma$; optically $-$; X: $c=1°$; $2V \doteqdot 65°–73°$, mean value $68\frac{1}{2}°$; moderate to strong dispersion; R.I.: $\alpha=1·751$, $\beta=1·786$, $\gamma=1·800$.
Min. Mag., vol. xxix, 1950, p. 115.
$H_2O > 105°C$: 0·24%. $H_2O < 105°C$: 0·09%. V_2O_3: 0·02–0·03%(s).

874. **Garnet.** Separated from hornfels (metamorphosed Skiddaw Slate; Ordovician). 600 yd N. 33° W. of Mosedale Bridge over River Caldew, Mosedale, Cumberland. 1-in. 23, 6-in. 48 S.W. (1566. Anal., W. F. Waters). E 23493.
Sp. gr.$=4·00$. R.I. for sodium light: $n=1·815$.
FeO: 30·3%. MgO: 2·3%. CaO: 1·1%. MnO: 5·3%.

875. **Garnet.** Separated from hornfels (metamorphosed Skiddaw Slate; Ordovician). 1130 yd N. 55° W. of Mosedale Bridge over River Caldew, Mosedale, Cumberland. 1-in. 23, 6-in. 48 S.W. (1567. Anal., W. F. Waters). E 23496.
Sp. gr.$=4·10$. R.I. for sodium light: $n=1·818$.
FeO: 29·1%. MgO: 2·5%. CaO: 1·2%. MnO: 6·9%.
See also No. 810.

876. **Garnet.** Separated from hornfels (metamorphosed Skiddaw Slate; Ordovician). 750 yd W. of Grainsgill Beck-Arm o'Grain junction, S. of High Pike, Cumberland. 1-in. 23, 6-in. 47 S.E. (1568. Anal., W. F. Waters). E 23521.
Sp. gr.$=4·08$. R.I. for sodium light: $n=1·822$.
FeO: 31·8%. MgO: 2·1%. CaO: 1·2%. MnO: 4·4%.

877. **Talc.** Separated from contact-altered Chapel Limestone of the Lower Limestone Group of the Carboniferous Limestone Series. Chapel Quarry, near Kirkcaldy, Fifeshire. 1-in. 40 Scot., 6-in. 35 N.E. (1210. Anal., C. O. Harvey). S 34826.
Fine-grained aggregate. R.I.: highest and lowest figures approximately 1·580, 1·535.
Min. Mag., vol. xxvi, 1942, p. 278.
SiO_2: 58·0%. Total Fe calculated as FeO: 0·7%. MgO: 29·4%. CaO: 1·2%. $Na_2O + Li_2O$: 0·2%. K_2O: 0·1%.

878. **Collophane.** Associated with dickite (No. 843) coating joints in Magnesian Limestone (Permian). 246–250 ft deep, Hesleden Dene Water Borehole No. 2, $1\frac{3}{4}$ miles E.S.E. of Castle Eden, Co. Durham. 1-in. 27, 6-in. 29 S.W. (1512. Anal., C. O. Harvey). E 22285.

Sp. gr.$=3\cdot00$. Brown, mainly isotropic but patchily birefringent. Optically $+$; 2V approximately $20°$; R.I. for sodium light: $\alpha=1\cdot608$, $\gamma=1\cdot615$.
Min. Mag., vol. xxviii, 1948, p. 341, pl. xx, fig. 6.
Approximate figures: $H_2O>105°C$: $1\cdot1\%$. $H_2O<105°C$: $1\cdot0\%$. CO_2, P_2O_5 present as major constituents. F not detected as a major constituent.

879. **Basaluminite.** In widened joints or fissures in Northampton Sand Ironstone (Jurassic). Lodge Pit, 2 miles S.E. of Wellingborough, Northamptonshire. 1-in. 186, 6-in. 39 S.E. (1437–8. Anal., C. O. Harvey).
White mineral consisting of basaluminite mixed with the fully hydrated form hydro-basaluminite. The basaluminite is compact with conchoidal fracture; the hydro-basaluminite is plastic but rapidly loses water in air and crumbles to powder which does not regain the plastic character on wetting. The air-dried material is fine-grained, powdery to compact. Sp. gr.$=2\cdot12$. Anisotropic, mean R.I.$=1\cdot519$. Another determination yielded: $n_1=1\cdot517$, $n_2=1\cdot521$.
Nature, vol. clxii, 1948, p. 565. *Min. Mag.*, vol. xxix, 1950, p. 10.
Analyses of two air-dried samples probably containing up to 15% allophane:—
1437. SiO_2: $2\cdot4\%$. SO_3: $15\cdot6\%$. Al_2O_3: 43%. Fe_2O_3: $0\cdot3\%$. P_2O_5: tr. H_2O (by difference) $38\cdot7\%$.
1438. SiO_2: $3\cdot6\%$. SO_3: $14\cdot2\%$. Al_2O_3: $41\cdot3\%$. Fe_2O_3: $0\cdot2\%$. P_2O_5: $1\cdot0\%$. H_2O (by difference) $39\cdot7\%$.

880. **Uraniferous hydrocarbon complex (thucolite).** E. wall of Laxey Lode, 100 fathoms level, S. of ' Engine ' shaft, Laxey Mine, Laxey, Isle of Man. 1-in. 46, 6-in. 8 S.W. (Anal., Chemical Research Laboratory).
Anthracite-like coal-black friable material. Strongly anisotropic hydrocarbon bearing smaller masses of moderately anisotropic hydrocarbon, a mineral or minerals of the uraninite group and accessory metallic sulphides. $H=2\cdot5$. Sp. gr. $(21°C)=1\cdot71$.
Bull. Geol. Surv. Gt. Brit., No. 3, 1951, p. 5; pl. i, figs. 1-3.
Ash content of hydrocarbon: $18\cdot67\%$. U_3O_8 in ash: $70\cdot5\%$. ThO_2: n.d.
Spect. det. of ash (percentages):—Al: $0\cdot15$–$0\cdot25$. As: $0\cdot3$–$0\cdot7$. Co: $0\cdot5$–$1\cdot5$. Cu: $0\cdot5$–$1\cdot5$. Fe: $0\cdot3$–$0\cdot7$. Ni: $0\cdot5$–$1\cdot5$. P: $0\cdot5$–$1\cdot5$. Pb: $0\cdot1$–$0\cdot3$. Si: $1\cdot5$–$2\cdot5$. W: $1\cdot5$–$2\cdot5$.

881. **Thucolite-type hydrocarbon.** From gold reef, Government Reef Series, Lower Witwatersrand System. Babrosco, 10 miles W. of Klerksdorp, western Transvaal, Union of South Africa. (Anal., Miss M. Corner, Chemical Research Laboratory).
Grey pitchblende-hydrocarbon complex with included galena, pyrite, etc. $H=2\cdot5$. Sp. gr. $(21°C)=1\cdot827$. Average radioactivity $10\cdot51\pm2\cdot0\%$ equivalent U_3O_8.
Bull. Geol. Surv. Gt. Brit., No. 3, 1951, p. 8; pl. ii, figs. 8–10.
Ultimate analysis of the hydrocarbon (percentages; mean values in parentheses):—C: $42\cdot3$, $43\cdot1$, $(42\cdot7)$. H: $2\cdot0$, $1\cdot45$, $(1\cdot7)$. N: $0\cdot2$. Halogen: tr. S: $2\cdot9$, $3\cdot3$, $(3\cdot1)$. Ash: $39\cdot4$, $38\cdot5$, $38\cdot2$, $(38\cdot7)$. Uranium content of ash: $30\cdot4$.

INDEX

The numbers refer to analyses and not to pages.

Aberdeenshire, Metamorphic limestone, 783; Titanaugite, 826.
Aberfoyle Slate Quarry, Perthshire, Slate, 796.
Achmelvich, Sutherland, Felsite, 737.
Adamellite, Argyllshire, 639; Cumberland, 644; Kincardineshire, 641.
Aegirine, 873.
Alston, Cumberland, Fluorite, 862; Iron ore, 866; Sphalerite, 852; Witherite, 868.
Amphibolite, Devonshire, 756.
Andesite, Ayrshire, 663; Cumberland, 665-6; Perthshire, 662; Somerset, 664. Trachyandesite, 660-1.
Anthophyllite, 827-8.
Antrim, Co., Obsidian, 630, 633-4; Porcellanite, 789; Rhyolite, 631-2.
Apatite-rock, Dumfriesshire, 790, 813-4.
Appinite, Inverness-shire, 657-9.
See also Granodiorite, 640.
Ardale Head Ironstone Mine, Cumberland, Iron ore, 864-5.
Ardnamurchan, Argyllshire, Granulite, 761.
Argyllshire, Adamellite, 639; Camptonite, 672, 674; Dolomite, 806-7; Garnet, 831; Gneiss, 763; Granodiorite, 647-8; Granulite, 761; Hornblende-schist, 755; Lamprophyre, 667-70; Lamproschist, 751; Metamorphic limestone, 781; Pegmatite, 620; Porphyry, 621-2, 624; Quartz-dolerite, 679; Quartzite, 803, 805; Slate, 792-4, 800; Tonalite, 642-3; Trachyte, 636.
See also Tiree.
Assynt, Sutherland, Aegirine, 873; Cromaltite, 746; Feldspar, 872; Grorudite, 735; Ledmorite, 740; Porphyrite, 741; Syenite, 736, 738-9; Vogesite, 742.
Auchinbee Quarry, Dumbartonshire, Quartz-dolerite, 676.
Ayrshire, Andesite, 663; Basalt, 693; Gabbro, 686; Picroteschenite, 719; Serpentine, 728; Soda-granite, 618; Spilite, 710; Syenite, 638; Tachylyte, 696; Theralite, 718; Trondhjemite, 618.

Badentoy Old Quarry, Kincardineshire, Adamellite, 641.

Balephetrish, Tiree, Argyllshire, Biotite, 833; Diopside, 824; Fassaite, 825; Marble, 782; Pargasite, 829.
Ballachulish Slate Quarry, Argyllshire, Slate, 792, 794.
Balvicar Slate Quarry, Argyllshire, Slate, 800.
Barkbeth, Cumberland, Slate, 797-8.
Barytocalcite, 870.
Basaluminite, 879.
Basalt, Ayrshire, 693; Kincardineshire, 695; Kinross-shire, 689; Perthshire, 690, 692, 694, 705; Skye, 697, 699-701. Contaminated, Cumberland, 809. See also Diabase, Dolerite, Mugearite, Palagonite-tuff, Spilite, Tachylyte, Teschenite.
Bechuanaland, Quartz-porphyry, 623.
Ben Loyal, Sutherland, Feldspar, 871.
Binsey, Cumberland, Andesite, 665.
Biotite, 833.
Blackness Borehole, Linlithgowshire, Thomsonite-pyroxene-garnet-rock, 788.
Blagill Mine, Cumberland, Barytocalcite, 870.
Boltsburn Mine, Co. Durham, Fluorite, 853; Siderite, 867.
Boracite, 845.
Bostonite, Orkney, 635.
Braehead Quarry, Midlothian, Quartz-dolerite, 681.
Breunnerite, 819.
Bristol, Galena, 846-8.
Brockhill, Worcestershire, Teschenite, 713.
Bulcote Borehole, Nottinghamshire, Olivine-analcite-dolerite, 711.
Bull Run Quarry, U.S.A., Dolerite, 691.
Byne Hill, Ayrshire, Soda-granite, 618.

Camptonite, Argyllshire, 672, 674; Orkney, 671, 673.
Carrick Hills, Ayrshire, Andesite, 663; Basalt, 693.
Carrock Fell, Cumberland, Basalt, contaminated, 809; Diabase, 706; Felsite, 629; Gabbro, 688; Granophyre, 615; Quartz-diorite, 650; Quartz-gabbro, 675, 743-4.

74

Wt. 2400   K4   1/65   Gp 3914   S.O. Code No. 62–384–0–65